It's all about the food
not the fork!

107 easy to eat
meals in a mouthful

Peter Morgan-Jones
with *Lisa Greedy, Prudence Ellis and Danielle McIntosh*

CONTENTS

FOREWORD BY MAGGIE BEER

I have been on the sidelines of Peter Morgan-Jones' journey with HammondCare and been very proud to have a little sense of ownership—having been part of choosing Peter for the role he holds as Executive Chef and Aged Care Food Ambassador. However, I could never have foretold just what an amazing catalyst for change Peter would be.

Peter has become a true change agent in a world that requires it. His knowledge of food and technique, and ability to think outside the square—aligned with a passion for flavour and a real empathy with people—led him to find food solutions for many who experience dysphagia. They were previously denied the simple pleasures of a beer or an ice-cream, which Peter has helped to restore. The difference this can make to an individual has to be seen to be believed.

When talking with cooks and chefs in aged care and carers in the community, the question so often asked is about ideas for finger food to give pleasure and nutrient in every bite particularly for those living with dementia. And here in this book we have so many ideas to share.

The leadership of Dr Stephen Judd has led this charge; Peter has around him every expert in the field so that together each element of specialised care can be considered when bringing about change. It is a recipe to be truly admired.

Peter has been a tireless advocate of the work of my foundation in trying to bring about change in the food life of elders in aged care and the community, on the wider canvas of society. His generosity in sharing his knowledge has been invaluable.

Aged care in all its forms is a complex world and whilst there are wonderful examples of forward thinking and great care, there is still a serious need to keep looking for how we can bring ongoing change.

There is nothing more seductive than being part of a movement of individuals and organisations doing great work and sharing their knowledge. It's truly how we create an appetite for life for everyone. This book is an example of that great work and shared knowledge which I know you'll enjoy.

Maggie Beer

INTRODUCTION– BRINGING BACK FINGERS

Peter Morgan-Jones

For many years as a chef I've enjoyed making delicious canapés for restaurants and events across the globe seeing 'first hand' how popular and acceptable it now is to eat on your feet, using your fingers.

So it wasn't surprising that amidst the success of our previous cookbook, *Don't give me eggs that bounce: 118 cracking recipes for people with Alzheimer's*, by far the greatest interest was in our approach to mid meals and finger foods!

As I and the other authors promoted the book around Australia, New Zealand and the United Kingdom, discussing our innovative recipe research and development, the conversation would continually turn to what seems such a simple idea—food that can be eaten with hands but is nutritious, appetising and beautiful!

Of course for some cultures, eating with your hands is the most traditional way to eat a meal but for others, especially in the West, a stigma has attached to eating this way, particularly in the past 100 years or so. Eating with your hands may be seen as bad manners or something for children.

Fingers before forks

History abounds with accounts of the development of implements for eating food, with tools for cutting meat discovered as far back as the Neolithic era. These knives developed into the most common eating accessory and it was only in more recent times that other tools became prevalent, such as the fork in Roman and Greek culture and chopsticks in China and then the rest of Asia.

It was common in medieval times to arrive at a banquet with your own dagger-style knife to eat with, having had it sharpened at the castle beforehand! The modern usage of forks probably began in Italy, may have been first associated with eating pasta and was finally given Royal sanction in 1633 when Charles I of England declared, 'It is decent to use a fork.'

Dispelling the stigma

'Coutelier' was the Old French term for knife and later was adapted to become the modern English term cutlery. An amazing array of etiquette has arisen around the use of cutlery, and this no doubt contributes to the stigma sometimes associated with older adults eating with their fingers. And while it might seem younger generations are less affected—with the rise of fast food— you might be surprised to know how many conversations I've had with family members who are concerned that their mum or dad is using their fingers at mealtimes.

Once given an explanation, with compassion, families soon see the positive impact of finger foods for people who struggle with the use of cutlery. We often explain how 'mum or dad' is now more independent, displays less anxiety at mealtimes and is usually eating more than they have done, with signs of healthy weight gain. Families are always quick to welcome these benefits and to view finger foods or hand-held meals differently.

Hand-held heroes

Having seen the positive change finger foods can make, we have made them the stars of *It's all about the food not the fork!* Every food recipe in this book can be eaten by hand and the following chapters provide fascinating insights into eating, ageing, dementia and finger foods.

A highlight of our recipes is the chance to provide a solution to the difficult area of modified meals—in a pureed, minced or soft form—presented in a finger food style. These really are hand-held heroes!

'A highlight of our recipes is the chance to provide a solution to the difficult area of modified meals—in a pureed, minced or soft form—presented in a finger food style. These really are hand-held heroes!'

01 SO MUCH MORE THAN PARTY PIES

Peter Morgan-Jones with Emily Colombage

Finger foods can open the door to more independence and improved nutrition for people living with dementia (and other conditions) who are struggling to use cutlery. They allow the person to control what is going into their mouth, returning a measure of dignity which may otherwise be lost.

Additionally these hand-held heroes can improve self-esteem and enjoyment in meal times. Importantly, finger foods for the older person are much more than party pies and sausage rolls. Rather than a quick dish for serving at a party, when we talk about finger foods in *It's all about the food not the fork!* we are referring to the regular provision of finger food as an alternative to 'cutlery food'—that is, food which requires a tool to eat it. A simple example of finger food is meatballs with baby carrots—this book is full of other finger food ideas and recipes.

Nothing childish about this food

Research shows that many people living with dementia may struggle to eat enough food. One reason is that mealtimes can be stressful and unpleasant occasions. Dining tables can be spaces of frustration and confusion where an individual struggles with arthritic hands, poor eyesight, unfamiliar objects and poor concentration. As a result

of these hurdles it can be difficult to fit into the usual routine of sitting down for three square meals a day.

In this context, finger food can be overlooked because it is misunderstood or simply not available. At times there are misconceptions about finger food being 'childish' or not nutritious enough but with careful planning and presentation this is not the case.

Fabulously flexible food

Finger foods can be utilised in many different ways. At a basic level, finger foods can be served across the three meals of the day —breakfast, lunch and dinner (see 'Meal plans'). Finger foods can also be made that suit people who are on texture modified diets and thickened fluids (see 'Proudly modified' and other recipe sections). They can be eaten seated or standing up and even while walking around (being mindful of falls risks).

Alternatively, finger foods can be given in smaller amounts, several times across the day. This approach of small and frequent meals, or grazing, might suit someone with a poor appetite or an individual who is very active. An active individual living with dementia may have higher energy requirements and six to eight meals per day may better meet their energy requirements

As a variant, finger foods may be used for an individual at certain times when normal meals are unsuitable. For example, if a person's tremors are worse at a particular time of the day, or when they are tired, finger food may be an easier means of feeding themselves.

Suzie lives with Alzheimer's disease. She also has a visual impairment, poor dexterity due to arthritis, has lost muscle strength and so is becoming more frail. Sometimes she expresses some frustration and aggression. She struggles to do things on her own but does not like receiving help. And it's quite clear—she is not enjoying mealtimes. When Suzie walks into the dining room, she swears and pounds her fist on the table. When a meal is placed in front of her she is often less than impressed! Suzie's carers are keen to try a different approach that might improve her mealtime experience as well as her nutrition. First, finger foods were introduced. It took Suzie some time to get used to eating without cutlery but then she embraced it. She starts her meals by touching the food then slowly taking little bites. After a few months of the new approach Suzie has gained a few kilos, which is fantastic, but even more importantly, she seems happier and more relaxed around the dining table.

What we've learned in practice

In introducing finger food in our cottages for people with dementia, we have learned not to overcrowd the plate and to keep presentation simple. More food can be added if the initial food has been eaten.

Rectangular plates worked well and we chose coloured plates to frame the food. For example, white sandwiches on white plates were untouched, but were consumed when placed on coloured plates where the sandwiches stood out. As a further help, a family member or friend sitting down and eating a similar meal offers positive cues to the person with dementia. A sense of sharing food and being in familiar company can have a calming effect.

Our experience shows some people really embrace using their fingers to eat food (though it might have taken a few meals before they got used to the change). It is important that the provision of finger food is carefully considered. We do not recommend a blanket approach for all individuals living with dementia, working with them in decision-making is vital.

Finger foods, along with smaller portions and more frequent meals, are very useful tools in a longer list of strategies to treat an older person with malnutrition. Some people will benefit from many strategies all at once, some from a selection. There are a range of strategies offered across each of the chapters in this book.

02 IMPACT OF AGEING AND DEMENTIA

Danielle McIntosh, Senior Dementia Consultant

To understand the importance of snacks, mid meals, smaller portions, and food that can be eaten with our hands, we first need to look at the impact of ageing and dementia on eating and drinking.

Ageing is a fact of life—a positive one of course! We all look forward to enjoying a long life and more of us are doing just that. In 2015, the number of people aged 65 years or older was 601 million, and by 2020 this number is estimated to reach 714 million (Population Reference Bureau, 2015). For the first time since records have been kept, the number of 'older' people will be higher than the number of younger people.

This is why supporting older people to live long, healthy and happy lives has never been more important and promoting the enjoyment of food and mealtimes is a key aspect—regardless of age or health condition.

What's going on inside?

There are some things science still does not understand about how and why the ageing process can impact on the experience and skills required for eating and drinking. What we do know is that as a person ages, they have a higher probability of:

- slower stomach emptying (meaning a person feels full for longer)

- reduced appetite

- reduced ability to taste salt and, possibly, bitter things

- reduced ability to smell

- increased reflux/heartburn

These experiences may be associated with a range of age-related physiological issues.

Muscles in the oesophagus may not work as efficiently. For example, some studies have shown that for seven to 22 per cent of older people and up to 45 per cent of people living in a nursing home, their muscles responsible for the peristaltic movement of food from mouth to stomach are less efficient. Similarly, reduced effectiveness of muscles that control the sphincter between the stomach and the oesophagus may impact appetite (for more on swallowing see 'Chapter 5').

Another factor is changes in hormone levels which can result in reduced appetite, as is the case with the hormone leptin in men.

Side effects from medications can also impact eating and drinking. For example, medication may result in a dry mouth which means there is not enough saliva to transport flavour molecules from food to the taste buds.

Wearing dentures and dental changes may also have an impact. Denture plates may act as a barrier to some of the taste buds inside the mouth.

Other more general aged-related changes can also impact on eating and drinking:

- reduced physical activity

- sensory impairments (failing eyesight, cataracts, glaucoma and poor hearing)

- physical changes and conditions (arthritis in joints especially fingers, decaying teeth, pain when sitting and/or moving)

Not everyone over a certain age will experience any or all of these issues, however the likelihood is more common as people age.

It's just not the same—changed food experience

Loss of appetite and feeling full for longer

Our appetite or feeling hungry has a big role in encouraging us to eat and drink, as well as influencing what we choose. If we don't feel hungry or still feel full, our drive to consume is not there. If this happens on a regular basis, the person may be missing out on essential nutrients as well as increasing the risk of dehydration.

If faced with a full-sized meal, a person who is not hungry or has low appetite may even feel sick at the thought of having to eat what is on their plate. This may especially be the case for a person who holds personal or religious beliefs that wasting food is bad or a sin.

Reduced ability to taste salt and other changes

Having a salt and pepper shaker on the dining table was once the norm for many people. In recent times, with a push to reduce salt intake, the salt shaker may have disappeared or people may feel societal (or spousal) pressure to not add more salt to their meal. Getting used to foods with reduced salt takes some time—our brains are programmed to recognise certain tastes and when the balance is changed, we have a tendency to not want to eat or drink it anymore. For a simple experiment, try a food that you like—baked beans, tomato juice, cheese—then try the reduced salt version. Did it taste the same? If you had the choice which would you prefer to eat/drink?

Older people often experience a reduction in the taste intensity of saltiness and so the flavour of food and drinks begins to taste wrong or not as nice. The balance of the flavours may also be affected, so foods may taste more bitter, sour or possibly even sweet.

Reduced ability to smell

Our appetites are stimulated by our sense of smell. Who can walk past a bakery or a barbecue and not feel hungry? The sense of smell has been important for our safety and health as well. From an early age we learn not to eat things that smell bad. We also learn to eat things that smell good. If you cannot smell food and drinks, your brain may lack the necessary sensory push to partake.

Some foods need to be smelt for their taste to be enhanced. Chocolate and tea are two good examples to try. First hold your nose, then take a bite of some chocolate (or chocolate biscuit), then after two to three seconds, release your nose. You should get a magnificent rush of lovely chocolate. You can do the same with a cup of tea. The experience of taste is enhanced through our sense of smell so if it is reduced, appetite can be affected.

Living with dementia

A person is more than a list of symptoms or conditions, and continues to be themselves regardless of changes that may occur. This is true in relation to their interaction with food and drink as well.

But it can help people with dementia and those who support them, to be aware of the common types and symptoms of dementia.

Different types of dementia

Alzheimer's Disease International (2015) estimates that there are about 46.8 million people worldwide living with dementia, and by 2030, this will rise to 74.7 million.

Dementia describes a range of conditions which affect the brain and symptoms may include:

- impaired memory

- disorientation

- poor concentration

- difficulty in naming and use of language

- impaired ability to learn, or recall learnt information

- difficulty with motor skills and coordination

- difficulty with thinking and in understanding or following a sequence

The significant impairments in brain function caused by dementia can be accompanied by personality and mood changes in the individual and changes in their judgement.

The most common types of dementia are Alzheimer's disease, vascular or multi-infarct dementia, frontotemporal lobe dementia (behavioural variant and semantic variant) and dementia with Lewy bodies.

There are other conditions that, as they progress, may also result in dementia. These include Parkinson's disease, Huntington's disease, infections (such as HIV and Creutzfeldt-Jakob disease) and excessive alcohol use.

More detail on dementia and other topics in this chapter are included in our previous book, *Don't give me eggs that bounce* and can also be obtained by speaking to your doctor, specialist or Alzheimer's advisory organisation.

Eating, drinking and the brain

Most of us don't think a great deal about the daily process of eating and drinking. We take it for granted that we can decide what we feel like and how best to fulfil desires for food or drink. When the brain is not functioning as it should, decisions and actions relating to when to eat, what to eat, where to eat and how to eat can be challenging for a person living with dementia.

The brain is the control panel for everything we do. There is not one movement or thought we have that does not involve the brain. We might see with our eyes, but it is the entire brain that makes sense of what we see. Take this example. Our eyes focus on an apple. The brain (occipital lobe) receives the signals from the eye and makes sense of them,

so that we can recognise what it is (limbic system) and can give it a name (temporal lobe)—an apple. The brain (temporal lobe) also recognises it as a food that is safe to eat as well as enjoyable (limbic system). It (parietal lobe) then sends signals to the muscles in the arm to reach out and pick the apple up, bring it to your mouth and then bite into it.

With dementia, the many connections and pathways needed to successfully eat and drink—from recognising the feeling of hunger and thirst to recognising food/drink and consuming it—can be damaged.

Encouraging independence

Both aged-related changes or the impact of dementia will usually, over time, lead to a loss of independence. Much can be done to support the person to keep their sense of independence, dignity and control by implementing good support strategies.

We also need to recognise that many people with dementia are older people and so difficulties they may have could be due to both dementia and ageing. Being aware of what is happening for the person, and why, is a good start before implementing any support strategies. The need or problem and the strategy should be a good match, otherwise everyone feels upset when it doesn't work as expected.

As you can see from this chapter, reduced appetite and changes to taste, among other things, are common experiences for older people and people with dementia. A strategy we have found to be well aligned with some of these needs, is to introduce hand-held or finger foods, as well as developing an approach to snacks that ensures they are both nutritious and appetising—making the most of every mouthful.

03 POSITIVE MEALTIME EXPERIENCES

Danielle McIntosh, Senior Dementia Consultant

Supporting a person living with dementia to eat and drink as independently as possible can make a positive difference to health, self-esteem and overall quality of life.

As you read about common eating and drinking difficulties and their impact on enjoyment and independence, you may notice how often the strategies of smaller but nutritious portions (snacks) and food that can be eaten without cutlery (finger foods) may not only help the person living with dementia to eat and drink well, but also have a profound effect on carers, family members and friends.

Much of the information in this chapter and throughout the book may have applications for people with other health conditions affecting swallowing, use of cutlery and level of appetite.

A person living with dementia may find the following activities difficult:

- recognising food and drink

- recognising or using cutlery

- performing dining 'steps' in the right order

- concentrating through a large meal

- adjusting to changed behaviours and habits

Eating and drinking difficulties can reduce the enjoyment of mealtimes, as they may:

- take longer

- require more concentration

- make a person feel different/disabled/ hopeless

- require different food/drink textures, crockery and cutlery

- isolate someone from friends and family

While utilising snacks and finger foods is the main focus of this cookbook, there are a range of other strategies that are helpful in supporting the person with dementia to eat and drink as independently as possible while addressing the most common issues. They are more fully addressed in our previous cookbook, *Don't give me eggs that bounce.*

Words and body language

A strategy that should be applied at all times is to pay attention to communication—the words you use and the way you use them as well as your body language. A person with dementia will often be sensitive to non-verbal signals so it is important that your body language matches what you are trying to say and do:

- use simple language

- speak in a clear voice and more slowly, leaving time for a response

- be appropriate and familiar with the person

- stay positive—avoid sarcasm, condescending and childish words and tones

- maintain choice by offering one or two alternatives.

- be relaxed and calm

- gain eye contact before and during conversations

- sit next to the person if they are sitting, walk if they are walking

- smile—it helps people relax—both the giver and receiver!

- show a person an item, don't just describe it, e.g. a sandwich on a plate

- listen carefully and read their body language as well!

Personal food knowledge

Knowing a person's unique food and drink preferences, both past and present, can make all the difference in creating successful mealtime experiences. Consider:

- likes and dislikes

- memories (good and bad)

- preferred times to eat e.g. dinner served at 6pm

- associations between meals and kinds of food

- mealtime routines (including from childhood) e.g. eating everything on their plate

- food seen as 'special' or comforting

- favoured dining locations for different meals e.g. breakfast in bed

- presentation preferences e.g. must use a tablecloth

For more advice on positive eating and drinking see *Don't give me eggs that bounce.*

Anita will not sit down to eat or drink. She constantly walks around and her husband, Ray, is concerned as she is losing weight. When offered something to eat or drink, Anita turns away and walks into the hallway looking for something. Then Ray recalled that Anita worked as a housekeeper in a large hotel for most of her working life. Ray engages his wife in helping to change the sheets on the bed, then says it's time for a morning tea break. Both Ray and Anita sit down outside, have a milkshake and a few sandwich triangles for 10 minutes, before Anita stands up and walks back inside. Ray changed his approach to eating and drinking to fit with Anita's life-long work routine of working then having a short break.

Supporting and adapting

While knowing the person is an excellent start to successful eating and drinking, finding the strategies that work can still require some trial and error. Having a range of things to try is recommended, as what may work today may not work tomorrow.

Whether you are planning to adapt your approach to meals to feature snacks or finger foods, or are considering other areas of support, these three keys are vital:

Physical environment

Physical layout and fittings are significant contributors to how well a space supports a person as they eat and drink. This includes the room they are in, table layout, seating, and positioning of food. The dining environment can give important clues to a person to help them understand the task, but, if not right, can also add to their level of confusion.

Social situation

Who is present, what they say and how they behave produces the social environment. A person living with dementia may pay attention to what people are doing to help understand what they should be doing. This can be a great way to help a person eat and drink well, but it can also hamper success as well.

Compensating for disability

Due to damage in the brain, some tasks need to be modified in such a way that the person living with dementia can be as independent as possible. We refer to this as enabling a person or compensating for the disability. For example, a common compensatory strategy is a ramp or lift. A person using a wheelchair is not able to use stairs, but installing a lift or a ramp enables them to get from one floor to another independently. The same principles can be implemented for a person living with dementia.

Strategies for success

The following strategies involve any or all of the three principles discussed above. More detailed explanations appear in *Don't give me eggs that bounce*.

Reduce noise and distraction

A person with dementia may be distracted by noise and movement in the environment, impacting on their ability to concentrate. This can cause frustration, confusion and inability or unwillingness to complete the meal. To address these concerns, keep the dining space quiet, turn off devices, limit (if possible) people at the table, consider who is the best person to sit closest, serve one course at a time and keep the table setting simple.

Cutting out cutlery

A person with dementia may not recognise, remember how to use, or be able to pick-up cutlery. For many families and friends this can be distressing, in turn increasing a sense of hopelessness and dependence. For an older person or a person with dementia, this can be embarrassing. Some useful strategies to try are:

- offering a reminder to the person to use their spoon, fork or knife

- only placing the cutlery necessary to eat the meal/course on the table

- placing the cutlery in the person's hand

- cutting up the person's food (in the kitchen, rather than at the table) so that only a fork or spoon is needed

- using cutlery the person is familiar with—if they have begun using adaptive cutlery, such as built up handles or angled spoons, this may cause additional confusion, so consider discontinuing their use

- sit and eat with the person who may benefit from watching the use of cutlery and the steps and movements of eating the meal

If these strategies are not effective, it is important to accept that cutlery should not be used anymore, as it may only increase frustration and helplessness. Instead, prepare foods that can be eaten without it— every recipe in this book is suitable for eating with fingers.

Greta always has superb manners and growing up was taught to always use cutlery —even to eat sandwiches. Greta's condition (dementia and rheumatoid arthritis) now make it impossible to use cutlery. Even though Evelyn prepares appetising and lovely looking finger foods on the dinner plate, Greta gets upset at not being able to use cutlery, often refusing to eat at all. Then Evelyn tried using a three-tiered stand (like those used in high tea) and a lovely platter dish to serve the finger food meals. The table was set nicely and the stand and platter were placed on the table. Greta was able to choose what she ate and would take two items at a time, before helping herself to more. Meal time became a high tea ritual, where eating dainty morsels with your fingers was customary.

Serving to suit

If a person does not want to sit and eat a meal, try:

- walking with the person, offering them finger foods

- leaving plates of finger foods, snacks and/or drinks around the house, so that the person can pick something up when they walk past

- offering regular snacks or finger foods, rather than a full meal

Peter walks the same 'path' around the house all day. Peter's wife, Colleen, leaves small bread and butter plates with slices of fresh fruit, cubes of cheese and crackers, on furniture along this 'path'. Colleen noticed that Peter sees the plates and eats one item before walking off. Over the course of the morning, the food would be gradually eaten. Colleen then refills the plates with other small items, as she knows Peter likes a variety.

Reduction in appetite as people age, as discussed in Chapter 2, can be common. For people living with dementia, it may be compounded by the type of dementia they have and/or the problems they may be experiencing with eating and drinking. If a person with dementia has had a negative experience with eating and drinking, while they may not remember the specific details, they are aware of having experienced an unpleasant feeling. It can be hard to win back the situation. Try:

- small meals frequently throughout the day (and night)

- providing food and drink when the person indicates they are hungry (including at night)

Keeping a diary of what the person eats and drinks each day may be useful when speaking with their doctor, dietitian, speech pathologist or other health professional.

Plate to notice and notice the plate

Older people need double the amount of light as a younger person. You can easily improve the lighting by:

- turning the lights on

- increasing the wattage in the light globes

- opening the curtains/blinds

Reduce any glare that may make sitting at the table uncomfortable—using a tablecloth is an easy way to stop glare from a shiny table surface. Also, sheer curtains can help to reduce glare from sun streaming through the window.

How you plate the food may also make a big difference. It is common for people with dementia to have difficulty distinguishing objects from the background, such as food on the plate. There are two simple rules you should follow when serving food on a plate, in a bowl or on a platter dish:

- make the food stand out from the plate

- make sure the plate stands out from the table

The greater the contrast between the food and the plate, the plate and the table and the

drink and the cup, the greater the chance that the person will see it clearly.

Finally, check things sometimes overlooked—does the person have on their glasses? Are the glasses clean? When was the last time the prescription was reviewed?

Plate to entice

A small selection of foods may invite a person to eat, rather than a large amount of one type of food. Having a mix of savoury and sweet foods on the plate may also encourage a person to eat.

Plate to share

Eating and drinking is most commonly done as a social activity. Sharing a meal with a loved one, a friend or colleague is much more than just eating. It can be a time to relax, to share what has happened in the day, and most importantly for a person with dementia, a time to reminisce about their lives. The recipes in this book are for all, not just for an older person or a person with dementia.

Contrasting colours.   Savoury and sweet options.   Discreet locks for chemicals.

Serve a plate that can be shared. Reaching out for a bite to eat could also help the person with dementia understand what to do, without making them feel helpless or dependent.

Change the view

Earlier in this chapter we referred to knowing the person and their routines, including knowing where the person might normally eat. This should always be considered as a first strategy. However, sometimes, it can be good to try a change. When the weather is nice, try sitting outside. Perhaps even have a barbecue—the smell of a barbecue can be very influential!

Other places to try could be:

- kitchen bench

- verandah/patio

- shaded spot in the garden

- a local park

- a local café/shopping centre (although be careful of too much noise and busyness)

- favourite beach or picnic spot

Safe and healthy eating

A person living with dementia may display changed behaviours, such as eating non-food items, seeking food constantly during the day or consuming large quantities of certain foods and drinks. This can be because they:

- have forgotten they have already eaten

- are not paying attention to or recognising the sensation of being 'full'

- may crave certain foods—most commonly sweet or high carbohydrate foods

- are unsure of where they are and what is happening, so take as much food as they can or store it in a safe place

To help manage consumption of inedible items, we recommend installing a discreet lock on kitchen cupboards, moving chemicals out of the kitchen and having food and drink clearly visible around the house to reduce searching.

To help manage overeating, develop or maintain mealtime routines, offer regular snacks throughout the day, pace the serving of courses and helpings, and serve smaller portions first before offering seconds (again small servings) if the person asks for more.

Overeating may occur because food is easily available. Strategies to manage this include:

- providing low calorie foods and snacks (such as fruit) in a familiar location so the person feels secure that food is always available

- portioning food in the cupboard or fridge such as having just two biscuits in a jar, rather than it being full

If you have other strategies to support healthy eating and drinking, we would love to hear about them. Sharing positive stories and strategies helps other carers and people living with dementia enhance their enjoyment of eating and drinking, so please contact the Dementia Centre—see 'Contacts and resources' or visit crackingrecipes.com

04 FINGER FOODS, DEMENTIA AND NUTRITION

Lisa Greedy, Accredited Practising Dietitian

Food that can be eaten by hand has long been an important strategy for assisting independent eating and managing small appetites. For people living with dementia where eating can be a challenge, finger foods have become a helpful tool in maintaining good food intake and nutrition.

Independence and eating

As mentioned in previous chapters, the degenerative effects of dementia often means over time that a person living with dementia loses independence with tasks including the ability to feed themselves effectively. Inability to use cutlery and recognise food can often mean that they rely on others to assist them to eat. This can cause mealtime stress to both the person and the carer.

The simple strategy of providing small manageable mouthfuls or finger foods can help to maintain independence as long as possible. It also allows control of the amount and speed of food into the mouth, which is not always possible when being assisted to eat. Choices of plates, set-up of environment and eating together can also assist in maintaining independence (see 'Chapter 3').

Eating more often is better

People living with dementia can find the task of sitting and eating a complete meal very challenging. Pacing or agitation can mean the person may not sit still for long periods, including mealtimes. They may have short attention spans and an appetite that changes day to day. Additionally, age related changes such as decline of taste, smell, chewing and swallowing can affect the ability to initiate or finish a meal. The strategy of providing small regular meals and finger foods means that a person is not locked into three square meals a day, allowing more opportunities to eat and absorb vital nutrients from their food.

Six to eight meals a day can really allow a person with a small appetite to go at their own pace. For a person living with dementia, providing mid meals (morning tea, afternoon tea and supper) can help fill nutritional gaps. As well, providing each portion 'one at a time' can reduce the feeling of being overwhelmed and the person is more likely to finish the meal.

Annie has been referred to the dietitian for losing weight and eating very little at lunch and dinner. She pushes away lovely cooked meals saying they are too much! She and her carer often become distressed, with the carer encouraging Annie to eat or trying to spoon the food in her mouth. The carer mentioned

Annie eats breakfast when given toast with butter and jam. Annie picks up a triangle of toast from the tray, then sits on her own and eats it. She then gets up again and reaches for the second triangle of toast. Annie is showing signs that she prefers food that she can pick up with her hands. It also appears she is overwhelmed by large portions. Annie is trialled with a plate of sandwiches with soft filling. This is first given on a shared plate and she responds that it is too much! She is then offered a triangle of sandwich on a butter plate 'one at a time' and this works the best. Annie eats one triangle and then is offered another. With this strategy Annie was able to eat a whole sandwich for lunch, followed by pieces of fruit for afternoon tea.

Making nutritious choices

Weight loss and malnutrition affects between 10 and 30 per cent of older people in the community and is a common struggle for those living with dementia. Malnutrition occurs when the body does not receive enough vitamins, minerals, energy (calories) and protein to maintain a healthy body. The result is a loss of muscle mass, strength and capacity to do everyday tasks such as getting out of bed, walking and getting dressed.

When choosing a finger food, careful planning is needed to ensure a balance of protein, energy and nutrients to ensure it is as nourishing as possible. When we are unwell and as we age, our dietary requirements change, so it is important to seek medical advice before making any significant changes.

For a person with a small appetite or losing weight, including foods which are naturally rich in protein and energy (refer to table below) can make the most of every mouthful they eat. As people with dementia are at risk of losing weight rapidly, avoid choosing low calorie or diet foods and choose full fat products. High calorie products such as butter or oil can be used to enrich cakes and biscuits. Foods containing protein can be incorporated with each meal or snack to give a good amount of protein to maintain muscles. Keep in mind that red meat, chicken and nuts can be difficult for some to chew, so these foods should be prepared so they are easy to eat.

High protein foods	High energy foods
Meat, fish and chicken	Cream
Eggs	Margarine, butter
Milk, cheese, yoghurt, custard (including soy and lactose-free)	Salad dressing, oil
Beans, legumes, nuts and seeds	Mayonnaise
Peanut or almond butter	Chocolate, sweets, ice-cream
Tin sardines, tuna, herrings	Bread, rice, pasta
Tofu and soy meat products	Spreads, jam, honey
Milk powder, protein powders	Fruit juice

Offering a large variety of fresh food including fruit and vegetables are also important as we are unable to gain sufficient nutrients from only one type of food. Many older people are at risk of low vitamin B12, calcium, vitamin D, iron and fibre levels so there should be a greater emphasis on these in the diet. Foods containing meat and dairy products, fruit, vegetables and grains are generally high in these nutrients. Vitamin D however is best absorbed from the sun.

A variety of colours and flavours might also grab the attention of the person living with dementia, encouraging them to eat that little bit more on the plate. Generally, older people enjoy sweeter foods. Although a balanced diet is ideal—if the preference is primarily for sweeter foods, ensure they are mostly from nourishing dairy, wholegrain or fruit-based sources. Additional supplement tablets or powders can be provided with the guidance of a doctor or dietitian in cases where the person is unable to eat the variety or quantity of food needed.

Special consideration is required when choosing finger foods for those with chewing and/or swallowing difficulties. A speech pathologist can recommend foods that are suitable. *It's all about the food not the fork!* provides recipes for hand-held, modified foods including pureed, minced and soft.

Refer to the 'Meal plan' section for finger food menu ideas utilising the recipes in this cookbook. Also, see the chart at the end of this chapter for a range of nutritious, easy to prepare snack ideas that can be eaten by hand.

What about eating too much?

Some people living with dementia can have insatiable or overeating behaviours, which may seem unhealthy or a challenge for carers. Remember that although overeating may seem alarming, if the person is very active their needs may be greater. If a person is enjoying their food and maintaining a healthy weight there is less concern, but consult your doctor or dietitian.

Offering one portion at a time may help. Encouraging social activities and non-food related tasks may also help vary the focus of overeating behaviours.

What to do with sticky fingers?

Being able to eat with your hands is an important step in independent dining for many people and to further support their dignity, some thought should be given to hygiene. Hand washing at the dining table can be facilitated by providing hand sanitiser, face cloth or finger bowls. This is partly for food safety but also promotes dignity.

Hydration and 'multipurpose' drinks

When talking about nutrition we cannot forget the importance of drinking and good hydration. Dehydration is when the body does not have enough fluid to carry out normal functions leading to infections, kidney problems and even coma. Dehydration is a common cause of hospitalisation so regular drinks are important. Additionally, a nourishing drink can support good nutrition for a person who is losing weight or unable to finish a meal. This is because a drink can be easier to manage than a meal, particularly for those easily fatigued. Providing a nourishing drink as part of a mid meal or alongside finger food can also increase the nutritional intake at that meal.

Milk or dairy-based drinks are generally a better nutritional choice compared to water, juice or tea as they contain more energy (calories), protein and vitamins. Simply making a milkshake with full-cream milk, ice-cream or yoghurt, milk powder and fruit can make a nourishing and enjoyable drink. Commercial supplement drinks can provide additional calories but should be considered with the guidance of a dietitian. Special consideration is needed for those with swallowing difficulties to ensure all drinks are suitable.

Nourishing drink ideas

There are many nourishing drink recipes available in *It's all about the food not the fork!* and ideas about how to use them in the 'Meal plan' section. But here are a few simple ideas:

- high protein milk (full cream milk + milk powder)

- smoothies made with fruit and yoghurt

- breakfast smoothies made with oats and nut butter

- Milo or Ovaltine drinks made with full cream milk

- flavoured milk

- iced chocolate and coffee

- hot chocolate and instant coffee made with full cream milk

- latte, cappuccinos

- thick shakes made with ice-cream

- fruit punch

- thick creamy soups

Tips for meal planning, eating and drinking

Mealtimes for a person living with dementia and their carers can be more successful when simple nutrition tips are incorporated into meal planning. These include:

- aiming for six to eight smaller meals rather than three big meals a day

- keeping the cupboard or fridge stocked with ready to eat meals and snacks, e.g. cheese cubes/ slices, deli meats, crackers, tins of sardines, milk drinks

- providing a variety of foods including high energy and protein food sources

- offering drinks such as milk or juice instead of just tea, coffee or water

- freezing baked items and bread for quick meals and snacks

- being creative in setting up the environment to promote eating

- increasing food amounts and frequency as activity levels increase

Role of a dietitian

A dietitian is a qualified expert in nutrition and food who conducts nutritional assessments for people who need support managing what they eat and drink. They can assist in improving weight management and promote a balance of vitamins, minerals and nutrient meal plans for clients.

For details on how to find a dietitian near you, see 'Contacts and resources'.

Meat and vegetarian alternatives

Meat that is dry may be difficult to eat, so try to keep it moist:

- chicken breast, cut into pieces
- hamburgers, meatballs, chipolatas, hotdogs or slices of meatloaf
- pieces of fish fillet (boned), fish fingers, small fishcakes
- vegetable burgers or vegetarian sausages
- slices of quiche or pizza
- hard-boiled eggs (quartered)
- cheese cubes
- slices of cheese on toast
- kebab
- roast beef sliced (cold cut) and wrapped around an asparagus spear
- small tart shells with hot meat inside
- individual meat pies and sausage rolls
- lamb cutlets
- sausages cooked and sliced into chunks
- salami sticks

Breads and cereals

Try different breads for variety, including wholemeal and white. Keep sandwiches small to make them easier to manage. Ideas include:

- buttered toast or bread fingers
- small bread rolls with butter
- sandwiches
- buttered crumpets or muffins
- crackers with butter or soft cheese
- biscuits
- scones, malt loaf, fruit loaf, teacakes or hot cross buns
- baguette sliced with topping (e.g.) tuna mayonnaise, cream cheese or egg mayonnaise
- slices of fruitcake or gingerbread
- waffles
- soft cereal bars
- chapatis or small pita breads
- crumpets
- wraps with soft filling e.g tuna mayonnaise and cucumber, wrap (not too thick) and slice like sushi roll
- pizza slices
- Nutrigrain
- Cornflake and Rice Bubbles cakes
- bircher muesli

Vegetables

Vegetables can be steamed, boiled or served raw, depending on what the person prefers and can manage:

- broccoli florets, cooked
- cauliflower florets, cooked
- carrot, swede or parsnip, cut into sticks or cubes
- brussels sprouts
- green beans or snow peas
- cucumber slices or sticks
- celery sticks or pieces
- cherry tomatoes or salad tomatoes, sliced or cut into wedges
- zucchini slices or sticks
- sliced peppers
- mushrooms
- corn fritters
- pastises
- potato gnocchi or vegetable ravioli
- cooked chat potatoes cut in half with filling
- individual tart shells with small chopped salad e.g. tomato and bococinni
- asparagus spears, cooked
- potato chips, wedges, potato cakes
- and scones
- celery sticks with cream cheese

Fruit

Fruit can be peeled if preferred. However, the peel may make it easier for the person to grip, particularly if it is a 'slippery' fruit, such as peach or nectarine:

- slices of apple or pear
- melon wedges
- pineapple chunks or rings
- orange segments
- slices of kiwi fruit
- strawberries or raspberries
- apricots (stone removed), cut into halves
- nectarines or peaches (stone removed), cut into slices or chunks
- seedless grapes
- bananas, whole or sliced
- small fruit muffins
- individual tart shell with cooked apple
- fruit smoothies in small cups
- dried fruit—ready-to-eat apricots, pears, apples or stoned prunes

Dairy

- Cubes of cheese
- Mini Bocconcini
- Cheese cake squares
- Ice-cream cones
- Soy ice-cream bars
- Frozen yoghurt bars
- Grilled cheese triangles
- Cream cheese dips and crackers
- Milkshakes in small cups

05 SWALLOWING AND DEMENTIA

Prudence Ellis, Senior Speech Pathologist

As people age, or as their body changes, they may begin to experience changes in their swallowing. This might also be a side effect of dementia or other medical conditions.

As discussed in *Don't give me eggs that bounce*, these problems with swallowing are called 'dysphagia.' Dysphagia is common, but not always a normal part of ageing. It may present as coughing, choking, clearing of the throat or a wet and gurgly voice while eating and drinking. One consequence of dysphagia can be aspiration.

Aspiration is the term used to describe food or drink 'going down the wrong way.' Most, if not all people are familiar with this sensation. It's uncomfortable and it can even lead to chest infections and aspiration pneumonia.

Improved comfort with eating

Speech pathologists are trained to improve comfort with eating and drinking, as well as to reduce the risk of aspiration and choking, through strategies, ideas and education.

One of the ways speech pathologists assist people with swallowing difficulties is to recommend modified foods (e.g. soft, minced or pureed) and thickened drinks. There's a perception that this means 'mushy' foods and 'gluggy' drinks. While they may look different, they can be amazingly creative and delicious—as recipes in this book show!

For a full explanation and description of modified foods and drinks, see the last section of this chapter. For more information on how to access a speech pathologist, see 'Contacts and resources'.

How dementia affects swallowing

Dementia as it advances can change the way the brain sends messages to the body and our swallowing responds to this change. There may also be generalised weakening of the muscles, and of the sense of smell (as well as other senses). Any of these can result in dysphagia.

Changes might also take the form of forgetting to chew, forgetting to swallow, food spilling out of the mouth, food feeling stuck in the throat or people forgetting how to feed themselves. These swallowing problems can take the form of food becoming stuck in the oesophagus (the feeding tube from the mouth to the stomach). This is when food will not pass through the oesophagus efficiently and may feel stuck or moving very slowly. It may be that only smooth or liquid foods will go down—a situation where a liquidised diet (see below) needs to be used. In these cases, a person may also benefit from smaller, more frequent meals to assist with passage to the stomach.

If you or a person you support is experiencing these problems, consult your doctor and/or a gastroenterologist, who can provide clinical assistance in this area.

Working with, not against

Supporting swallowing which may be affected by dementia involves working alongside the features and behaviours of dementia. For example, if a person eats with their fingers—offer finger food. By providing appropriate food choices, eating with your fingers becomes socially acceptable rather than a 'behaviour.' Suddenly a person is empowered to eat in the way that is most independent for them¬—after all *It's all about the food not the fork!*

Finger food and swallowing

Finger food offers a helpful strategy for people with dementia and swallowing difficulties. It allows them to maximise independence and capitalise on their remaining fine motor control. Perhaps less better understood is that finger foods also support safe swallowing. The hand-to-mouth motor program that is used when eating finger food is well established. This helps to coordinate moving food to our mouths, preparation of a swallow, and timing of a swallow—something which may be challenging for people with dementia.

Some people may benefit from finger foods but also require modified diets such as soft, minced or pureed and thickened fluids. This is an opportunity for creativity as seen in the modified finger food and thickened fluid recipes in *It's all about the food not the fork!* Often, the provision of smaller, more frequent meals can assist with problems in the oesophagus while also helping with nutrition (see Chapter 4.)

The family that swallows together...

Eating together is not just helpful for providing cues for a person living with dementia on how to use cutlery or the steps of eating, as mentioned in previous chapters. This 'therapeutic eating' can also support the person with swallowing difficulties as they may be prompted by your example in bringing food to their mouth, opening their mouth, chewing well and timing their swallow, all of which may support safer swallowing and increase food intake. While you may still need to offer some assistance, this is much more natural when you are sharing the meal together.

Strategies for 'unique methods'

People with dementia may display some unique methods of eating and swallowing that can at times be uncomfortable for those around them. Here are some strategies that may assist with these unique methods.

Symptom	Suggestion
Spitting out bits of food	Provide a napkin on which to place the food
Holding food in the mouth	Offer sips of drink between mouthfuls of food
Difficulty chewing	Encourage the person to swallow again before taking another mouthful
Overfilling the mouth	Use small cutlery
Food spilling out of the mouth	Consider giving food in smaller, more frequent portions
	Consider giving food in smaller, more frequent portions
	Eat together and help with portioning of the meal by providing verbal prompts, like 'slow down' and 'have a drink'
Food getting stuck in the throat	Alternate between food and drinks
Forgetting to swallow and not sensing food in the mouth	Alternate between a teaspoon of food and an empty teaspoon
	Try foods of different tastes, textures and temperatures
Coughing/throat clearing/gurgly voice during or straight after eating or drinking	Ensure the person is seated fully upright and not tilting to one side

Safe swallowing is for everyone

Safe swallowing is an essential part of eating and drinking for everyone, not just for people with dementia. Some of the strategies which we should all implement are:

- sit upright and alert in a chair for eating and drinking

- sit upright for 20-30 minutes after finishing a meal

- maintain good oral care (this means maintaining a pink and moist mouth, brushing teeth twice a day and seeking oral gels for dry mouth)

- take medications with prescribed diet and fluids (modified or normal) e.g. if on a puree or minced diet, medications should be crushed. If on thickened fluids, medications should be given with those fluids (as well as being crushed, if relevant). Consult your pharmacist before altering any medication.

Risk and choice

It is very important to recognise that everyone deserves a choice about what they eat and drink. A speech pathologist will seek to make recommendations for their client, based on best practice but sometimes people will choose to eat and drink anything they desire, regardless of the risk. It's crucial that clinicians, clients, and carers have honest and open conversations about the balance between risks and quality of life. Even the simplest things can make a difference if everyone works together!

John has had a stroke and also has mild dementia. After the stroke, his family realised he has swallowing problems and that he may have had them previously. John has also had his stomach removed, and has to eat smaller, more frequent meals to help prevent reflux and to make sure the food goes down well. Daughter Kate prepares all John's meals and finds she often worries if John is over or under-eating. A minced diet and mildly thick fluids help prevent food and drink going into John's lungs. Kate also helps prevent aspiration pneumonia by making sure her dad has good oral care. Kate works very hard to make sure John eats safely, and that the food is similar to that which she provides for her mum. She knows it can't be too soft or too hard and she also sees the benefits of including finger food options for her dad, who can no longer manage cutlery. He especially likes malt biscuits with lots of jam and finds these and other finger foods easier to pick up and eat.

Defining modified diets and fluids

As with *Don't give me eggs that bounce*, it's important to use the standard definition of each modification. Since its publication, there have been some additions to the classification of diets and fluids that deserve mention.

The numbers and labels of some modified diets and fluids have changed. There has been work to standardise the terminology internationally. If adopted globally, this would mean that 'Texture B' in Australia is the same as 'Texture B' in America, or in any other country. The benefits are obvious and the change welcome. This is a very new change and at this stage is optional for use.

Also, previously with the Australian standards there was only smooth pureed, minced and moist, soft, and regular food; and thin, mildly thick, moderately thick, and extremely thick fluids. There is now one extra fluid level and one extra food level.

Firstly, 'slightly thick' has been created as an additional fluid level. It sits between thin and mildly thick and is used in special circumstances—it is not standard practice for major clinics. A 'liquidised' consistency has also been added which is used to indicate a smoothie of food (that is, a savoury smoothie). This is a very useful addition, and has widespread application for people with dementia, who may be very comfortable drinking fluids, but not so keen on eating! Additionally, smooth pureed is now referred to simply as 'pureed.' Just like any other modified food or fluids, knowing how to apply these modifications requires consultation with a speech pathologist.

The new classifications are numbered from 0 to 7, and the numbers overlap between fluids and foods that share similar texture properties (see next page). This means that liquidised foods are expected to have the same thickness as moderately thick fluids (texture 3), and that pureed foods should have the same thickness as extremely thick fluids (texture 4). The following information is based on the explanations of the new international terminology.

Fluid consistency

Level 0: thin fluids—regular or unmodified fluids.

Level 1: slightly thick (new addition)—thicker than water, may occur naturally (e.g. fruit nectar).

Level 2: mildly thick (level 150/nectar)—runs through the prongs of a fork continuously and leave a thin coating, thicker than fruit nectar.

Level 3: moderately thick (level 400/honey) —drips slowly in dollops through the prongs of a fork.

Level 4: extremely thick (level 900/pudding) —will sit in a mound on a fork; a small amount may flow through and form a tail below the fork prongs but it does not flow or drip continuously.

Food textures

Level 3: liquidised (new addition)—smooth, lump-free and liquid food, which is the same consistency as moderately thick fluids. This diet provides an in-between level between food and fluids, and can really help those that prefer drinking, rather than eating, also making sure that the food is not just watered down and is rich in nutrients.

Level 4: pureed—smooth, lump-free food that holds its shape on a spoon; the same consistency as extremely thick fluids.

Level 5: minced—has lumps up to 0.4cm (4mm) which are moist and soft (and not sticky). Lumps should be mashable with your tongue.

Level 6: soft—food with lumps up to 1.5cm in size. Food should be tender and moist, and mashable with the back of a fork.

Level 7: regular—normal/unmodified food.

RECIPES

R   Regular diet, no restrictions

S   Soft

M   Minced

P   Pureed

T   Thin fluids, no restrictions

Th1   Mildly thick

Th2   Moderately thick

Th3   Extremely thick

BREAKFAST

Breakfast is now finger-licking great, thanks to these appetising recipes that transform all our breakfast favourites into high energy and high nutrition finger foods.

BREAKFAST COOKIES

Serves 24 cookies/12 serves
Prep 10 minutes
Cook 16 minutes

2 cups rolled oats
1 cup plain flour
1 tsp baking powder
1 tsp baking soda
⅓ tsp cinnamon
½ tsp sea salt
1 can drained cannellini
   beans
¼ cup unsalted soft butter
1 cup soft brown sugar
1 egg
3 tsp vanilla
½ cup chocolate chips
½ cup raisins
½ cup finely chopped walnuts

Preheat oven to 180°C. Place the oats in a food processor and pulse until fine. Add the flour, baking soda and baking powder, cinnamon and salt and process further until combined.

Remove and place in a large bowl, wash the beans and dry. Place in a food processor and pulse until a rough puree. Add the butter, brown sugar, egg and vanilla and blend, scraping down the sides as you go. Fold in the nuts, chocolate chips and raisins.

Place large spoonfuls of dough onto baking sheets sprayed with a little olive oil. Dampen hand and flatten down the cookies slightly with fingers and bake until golden brown, about 12 – 14 mins.

Allow to cool slightly and place on cooling tray. These will keep at room temperature sealed in a jar for quite a few days.

Tip: **These cookies are packed with fibre and protein and are the perfect breakfast snack for people who are very active.**

CONTINENTAL BREAKFAST

Serves 2
Prep 5 minutes
Cook 5 minutes

1 hard-boiled egg (peeled)
(See 'Basic recipes')
80g mild cheddar cheese,
diced into 3cm cubes
4 grilled button mushrooms
4 cherry tomatoes
80g sliced leg ham,
   cut into half
2 pre bought cocktail
   croissants
6 x 3 cm cubed rock melon

This a great grazing breakfast and is relatively stable at room temperature for an hour.

Any combination can be added, halve the egg and divide all ingredients equally on 2 plates. Roll the ham so it can be easily picked up.

Cook the croissants and allow to cool cut in half and butter and serve with the breakfast

Tip: **Salami is also a great option for grazing, or wedges of frittata, any type of cubed fruit and any type of soft bread.**

BACON AND EGG CUPS

Serves 6
Prep 10 minutes
Cook 10-15 minutes

12 rashers of streaky bacon
6 eggs
2 tomatoes, sliced
6 slices of bread
Parsley, chopped
Sea salt flakes and ground
   white pepper
Olive oil spray

Preheat oven to 170°C.

Liberally grease a 6 cup muffin pan with the oil. Over a medium heat, gently fry the bacon, be very careful to only partially cook it and not let it get crispy, as it needs to be pliable. Drain on paper towel.

Use a round cutter to cut 6 slices of bread and place in each of the muffin cups. For each muffin cup, wrap 2 rashers of the bacon loosely around the edges of the tin so that they are slightly overlapping and form a 'cup' around the edges. Lay a slice of tomato on each round of bread.

Crack an egg in each cup, then season with salt, pepper and parsley. Gently place in the oven for 10-15 mins, watching carefully for the last 5 mins. Once the white has just set, they are done.

BACON MUFFINS WITH CREAM CHEESE & SPINACH

Serves 5 muffins/serves
Prep 20 minutes
Cook 15 minutes

½ tbsp rice bran oil
3 smoked streaky bacon
    rashers, roughly chopped
1 packed cup baby spinach
    leaves
125g plain flour
¼ tsp sea salt
1 tsp baking powder
¼ tsp bicarbonate soda
40g strong cheddar,
    coarsely grated
1 egg, beaten
40g unsalted butter,
    melted and left to cool
125ml buttermilk
Patty cake papers/cases
40g cream cheese, mixed
    with a little milk, to make
    into a paste.

Preheat oven to 180°C. Grease and line a muffin tin with muffin cases.

Heat the oil in a pan and fry the bacon for 3 – 4 mins until crispy. Remove with a slotted spoon and set aside on kitchen paper so to drain as much oil as possible.

Meanwhile, wilt the spinach by putting it in a colander in the sink and pouring boiling water from a kettle over the leaves. Refresh under cold water, then use your hands to squeeze out as much liquid as you can. Transfer to a chopping board and chop finely.

Combine the flour, salt, baking powder, bicarbonate soda and cheese in a large bowl. In a separate bowl or large jug, mix the beaten eggs, melted butter and buttermilk. Pour the egg mixture over the dry ingredients and stir using a spatula until just combined.

Fold in the cooled bacon and chopped spinach until evenly distributed (but the batter remains lumpy). Note: Incorporating all the ingredients quickly without over-mixing will give light, fluffy muffins.

Spoon the batter equally into the cases. Scatter the remaining cheese over the cases. Bake for 15 mins until golden and risen, or until skewer comes out clean. Remove the muffins from the tin and place on a cooling rack.

Using a spatula, place the cream cheese frosting onto the cooled muffins and serve immediately.

Tip: **Great for morning or afternoon tea as well.**

BACON AND EGG PIE

Serves 6
Prep 45 minutes
Cook 45 minutes

250g shortcrust pastry
(see 'Basic recipes')
6 eggs
1 cup cream
4 rashers bacon diced
1 cup grated mozzarella
3 tbsp chopped flat leaf
   parsley
2 tsp Dijon mustard
4 rashers bacon rind
   removed
2 tsp sea salt flakes
½ tsp ground white pepper

Preheat oven to 180°C. Roll out pastry on a floured surface until 3mm thick. Place the pastry into a greased and lined 25cm pie tin and refrigerate for 30 mins, remove from refrigerator and trim excess pastry around edge.

Prick pastry with a fork and place baking paper on top of pastry. Place 500g raw rice in base of pastry and place in a preheated oven at 180°C and cook for 8 mins. Carefully remove the paper and rice and place back in oven for a further 8 mins then remove and allow to cool.

Place the eggs, cream and seasoning in a bowl and whisk until combined. Heat a little olive oil in a frying pan and cook the diced bacon lightly and then add the bacon when cooled to the egg mix. Add the chopped parsley, grated mozzarella and Dijon mustard.

Carefully pour the mixture into the pastry case. Place the four thin rashers on the top of the mix and bake for 30 – 35 mins in oven. Check to see if the mix has set. If still runny place back in oven until firm.

Allow to cool slightly before serving.

Tips: **This is delicious cut into wedges and served hot or cold. ~ It is an ideal snack food that can be eaten with the hands and served for breakfast, lunch or dinner.**

HAM & CHEESE ENGLISH MUFFIN FRENCH TOAST

Serves 2
Prep 5 minutes
Cook 5 minutes

2 eggs
½ cup cream
2 English muffins
80g grated cheddar cheese
100g sliced leg ham
½ tsp sea salt flakes
Pinch ground white pepper
1 tbsp butter
Dash of olive oil

Open the muffins in half, mix the eggs and cream, season with the salt and pepper and place in a ceramic bowl. Grate the cheddar as fine as possible into the egg mixture and mix through.

Immerse cut side of muffins and soak for approximately 3 mins. Turnover and soak crust side for 2 mins.

Heat the oil in a frying pan with the butter, carefully remove the muffins and place in hot oil carefully and cook until golden brown. Turnover and cook the other side until golden brown.

Remove and place 50g of leg ham on each muffin half. Serve with tomatoes or grilled mushrooms.

Tips: **Can also be served as a sweet version. Omit the salt and pepper and add 2 tbsp caster sugar. Switch the ham and cheddar for ricotta cheese and serve with large diced pieces of fruit or hulled strawberries.**

FARMWORKERS BREAKFAST SKILLET

Serves 2
Prep 5 minutes
Cook 10 minutes

1 rasher of bacon,
  rind removed
1 large field mushroom,
  quartered
8 bite-sized cherry tomatoes
2 thin pork sausages twist
  each in half and cut on
  twists
2 hard-boiled eggs
3 small cooked chat potatoes
  halved
Extra virgin olive oil
Sea salt flakes and black
  pepper to taste
1 tsp chopped thyme leaves

Cut rind off the bacon and cut bacon into half and roll into tubes and skewer with a tooth pick.

Pour a little olive oil in a non-stick frying pan and bring to heat. Start browning the sausages, then add the bacon followed by the field mushroom pieces.

Cook on all sides until almost cooked and then lastly add the cherry tomatoes for 30 seconds just to sear the skin. Season with sea salt flakes and cracked pepper and sprinkle over the thyme.

Arrange a selection of breakfast treats on 2 plates including the boiled eggs (quartered).

BREAKFAST TORTILLA

Serves 2
Prep 5 minutes
Cook 8 minutes

100g good quality pork
   sausage
¼ Spanish onion, sliced thinly
4 medium button
   mushrooms, halved
4 free-range eggs
2 tbsp cream cheese or
   ricotta
½ tsp sea salt flakes
¼ tsp ground white pepper
1 cup washed baby spinach
   leaves
1 tbsp chopped chives
4 tbsp extra virgin olive oil

Remove the skin from the sausages and heat 1 tbsp of the oil in a 25cm non-stick frying pan. Stir to ensure all the sausage is cooked. Remove and allow to cool.

Add another tbsp of olive oil in the same frying pan and brown the onions and mushroom halves. When cooked, add to the sausage mince.

Mix eggs, ricotta and seasoning into a bowl. Add the cooled sausage, mushroom and onion mix. Add chopped chives.

Wipe clean the frying pan, add 1 tbsp of extra virgin olive oil and heat, add the baby spinach and stir until wilted. Remove spinach and squeeze dry removing any excess liquid and then add to the egg mix.

In the same frying pan heat the last 1 tbsp of extra virgin olive oil, pour the egg and sausage mix into the frying pan and cook until the edges start setting, do not stir.

The tortilla can be then placed under a grill in the frying pan (make sure frying pan does not have a plastic handle) until the top is golden brown. Another method is cover pan with large plate and carefully invert the tortilla and place the top side facing down into frying pan and continue to brown.

Tips: **Delicious served hot or cold in wedges, for lunch or breakfast. ~ It can be served with bacon rolls and cherry tomatoes as a snack style breakfast. ~ A choice of fillings can also be used. ~ It is great with smoked trout and asparagus for a lunch.**

ELEVENSES*

It's not only Winnie the Pooh and hobbits who need those extra snacks in the day. These mini meals might actually become the main way of dining for many people who can no longer enjoy larger meals. So enjoy these masterful recipes several times across the day or as more traditional morning or afternoon tea and supper.

* For elevenses, Winnie the Pooh prefers honey on bread with condensed milk while hobbits will eat just about anything.

BEAN QUESADILLAS

Serves 8 pieces
Prep 10 minutes
Cook 10 minutes

Rice bran oil for frying
1 can of red kidney beans,
   rinsed and drained
   and mashed
2 cups grated cheddar
   cheese
250g punnet cherry
   tomatoes, sliced
2 large flour tortillas
½ tbsp chopped parsley
1 tsp oregano

Spread the bean puree over one of the tortillas, sprinkle the sliced tomato and cheese and herbs over the bean and tortilla. Season with sea salt and pepper. Place the other tortilla on top and refrigerate for 10 mins.

Place 1cm in depth of rice bran oil in a large frying pan that will accommodate the tortilla. Carefully place the quesadillas in the hot oil and cook for 2 mins, weighing it down with a smaller frying pan or saucepan. Carefully remove and turn over the quesadillas repeating the process.

Drain on paper towel, cut into 8 pieces and serve straight away.

CHEESE, HAM & CHIVE CROQUETTES

Serves makes 14,
3 per serve
Prep 10 mins
(+ 75 mins resting)
Cook 10 minutes

250g grated mozzarella
100g plain flour
80g finely diced ham
2 tbsp finely chopped chives
¼ tsp cayenne pepper
1 free range egg lightly
    beaten
2 tbsp cornflour
1 tsp sea salt flakes
1/4 tsp ground white pepper

Place the cheese, 70g of the flour, ham, eggs, cayenne pepper and seasoning in a bowl and mix to combine. Roll mixture into about 14 balls and place on baking paper covering a plate and refrigerate for 1 hour.

Combine the remaining cornflour and plain flour on a plate and roll the cheese balls in the flour mix. Place back in the refrigerator for 15 mins.

In the meantime heat rice bran oil in a large saucepan, bring heat up until a piece of bread turns brown within 40 seconds of dropping in hot oil. Deep fry croquettes in batches until golden brown—about 4 – 5 mins, drain on absorbent paper.

WHOLEMEAL RASPBERRY BARS

Serves 12 bars/serves
Prep 20 minutes
Cook 45-50 minutes

2 cups whole meal flour
½ cup wheat germ
½ cup castor sugar
Pinch of salt
250g butter, cubed
   and softened
½ cup rolled oats
½ cup walnuts
¼ cup brown sugar
1 tbsp flax meal
250g jar raspberry jam
125g punnet raspberries
Juice ½ lemon

Line and grease a 24cm x 24cm square tin, and preheat oven to 170°C.

Add the flour, wheat germ, sugar and salt to a kitchen mixer, and slowly beat in the cubes of softened butter. Reserve 1½ cups of this mixture and press the remainder into the tin. Bake for 15-20 mins.

Using a food processor, blitz the walnuts until fine. Add the nuts, along with the oats, brown sugar, and flax meal to the remaining flour/butter mixture. In a small bowl, mix together the raspberries, jam and lemon juice.

Spread the raspberry mixture over the base as soon as it comes out of the oven, then the nut mixture on top, pressing slightly. Bake for 25 – 30 mins.

Once golden brown, remove and leave to cool in the pan. Cut into 12 pieces and store in the refrigerator.

HOT SMOKED SALMON AND MASCARPONE PATE

Serves 3
Prep 10 mins

125g mascarpone or
  cream cheese
½ tbsp chopped flat leaf
  parsley
2 tbsp tarragon leaves
  chopped
½ tsp grated lemon zest
½ tbsp lemon juice
½ tbsp Dijon mustard
150g hot smoked salmon
  with skin removed
Cracked black pepper
30g butter

Place the mascarpone, mustard, lemon zest, lemon juice in a food processor and blend until smooth.

Flake the salmon checking for any bones vigilantly and add to the mascarpone mix and pulse until blended, add the herbs and season to taste.

Transfer the mixture to a ramekin or bowl and smooth the top. Melt the butter and allow to cool slightly, pour on top and place in the fridge to set.

Tips: **For regular diets, this is ideal served with brown bread and butter as a sandwich filling or on toast as a savoury toast topping. ~ It is also great for filling cucumber cups. ~ Nice also with water crackers.**

ROASTED BABY POTATOES WITH ITALIAN SAUSAGE

Serves 4
Prep 5 minutes
Cook 40 minutes

12 baby potatoes (chat
    potatoes, Jersey royals)
    (depending on size)
2 thin Italian sausages
1 tbsp extra virgin olive oil
1 tsp thyme leaves chopped
1 tsp rosemary leaves
1tsp sea salt flakes
2 tbsp grated parmesan
1 spring onion

Preheat oven to 200°C.

If potatoes are bigger than 2 bites halve them. In a frying pan or barbecue cook the Italian sausage, allow to cool and slice into large 2 bite pieces.

Put the baby potatoes in a roasting tin and sprinkle with the oil and sea salt and herbs. Mix together with hands to coat the potatoes and roast for 30 – 40 mins until cooked. As soon as potatoes are cooked add the cooked sausage and leave in oven for 10 mins or until the sausage is warmed through. Remove and grate parmesan on the potatoes.

Tips: **Any combination of meat and other vegetables can be added. ~ Button mushrooms are a great addition. ~ It can also be served with sour cream and sweet chilli sauce as a side—if appropriate for the person.**

BEC'S BANANA & COCONUT BREAD

Serves 12
Prep 10 minutes
Cook 1 hour

1 cup gluten-free or
   self-raising flour
1 cup shredded coconut
1 cup buckwheat flour
½ cup raw sugar
2 tbsp extra virgin olive oil
3 large ripe bananas
½ cup coconut oil
½ cup coconut cream
3 eggs
1 tsp vanilla essence
2 tsp ginger powder
2 tsp baking powder
½ tsp baking soda
Shredded coconut for
   the topping

Preheat oven to 180°C.

Mix all the dry ingredients together, making a well in the middle in a ceramic bowl. Mix the bananas, eggs, coconut cream and vanilla in a food processor. Pour the liquid mixture into the well with the oils and mix together with a wooden spoon.

Line a large loaf tin with baking paper and pour in the mix. Sprinkle the shredded coconut on the top.

Cook the bread until firm to touch, about 1 hour in total, on centre shelf in oven. Remove and allow to cool on a cooling rack.

Tips: **Cut into slices and freeze, it keeps well for 5 days wrapped in refrigerator. ~ Great toasted with butter.**

CINNAMON STICKIES

Serves 9 biscuits
Prep 15 minutes
(+ 20 mins resting)
Cook 30 minutes

Base
1 cup plain flour
1 cup wholemeal flour
1 tbsp baking powder
1 tbsp caster sugar
¼ tsp sea salt
¾ cup milk
¼ cup olive oil

Filling
½ cup soft brown sugar
½ tsp cinnamon
¼ cup sultanas
¼ cup chopped pecans

Sticky stuff
2 tbsp butter
¼ cup soft brown sugar
1 tbsp maple syrup

Preheat oven to 200°C.

For the 'sticky stuff' place all ingredients in the bottom of a greased 20cm square cake tin. Leave in oven for 10 mins and stir to combine ingredients in bottom of pan.

Remove from oven, meanwhile make the biscuit, combine the flours and baking powder and sugar and salt in a bowl. Add the milk and olive oil and stir by hand until a soft dough is formed. Do not overmix or it will be like a board!

Flour a surface and roll out to roughly a 20 x 35cm rectangle. Sprinkle with the brown sugar cinnamon, sultanas and pecan nuts. Start from the long side roll over like making a sushi roll.

Allow to chill in refrigerator for 20 mins, remove and cut the roll into 9 slices using a sharp serrated knife. Place the cut sides down into the tin and submerge into the sticky stuff. You should have 3 rows of 3 in the square cake tin.

Bake for 20 mins and once cooked invert and serve. These are great with cream.

DATE, APPLE & SULTANA SLICE

Serves 10 slices/2 per serve
Prep 10 minutes
Cook 20-25 minutes

175g softened unsalted
  butter
1 cup brown sugar
1 cup self-raising flour
1 tsp ground ginger
1 tsp ground cinnamon
Zest of 1 lemon
3 apples, cored and sliced
1 cup sultanas
1 cup chopped pitted dates
1 tbsp demerara sugar

Heat oven to 180°C, grease and line with baking paper a 19cm x 29cm slice pan.

Beat butter and brown sugar until light and fluffy; sift together the flour and the spices. Add this to the butter mix to make a batter and mix well.

Chop the dates and slice the apples and add them to the batter along with the sultanas.

Place slice batter into lined baking pan and sprinkle top with the demerara sugar. Bake in oven for 20 – 25mins or until a skewer inserted into middle comes out clean.

PEANUT & SULTANA COOKIES

Serves makes 12-14
Prep 10 minutes
Cook 12 minutes

125g unsalted butter
½ cup caster sugar
1 free range egg
1¼ plain flour sifted
1 tsp baking powder
120g raw peanuts chopped
   roughly
80g sultanas

Preheat oven to 180°C. Place butter and sugar in a bowl of a mixer and whisk until light and creamy, add the eggs and mix. Fold in the flour, sultanas, chopped nuts and baking powder.

Shape tbsp of biscuit dough into rounds on baking tray lined with baking paper. Bake for 10 – 12 mins until golden brown. Cool on a cooling rack. Store in an airtight jar.

Tips: **Other types of nuts can be added to replace the peanuts. ~ Nuts are a great source of protein.**

HOME
SWEET
HOME

PORTUGUESE TARTS

Serves 6
Prep 10 minutes
Cook 15-20 minutes

125g approx. frozen puff
pastry sheets
1 tsp plain flour
½ tbsp cornflour
80ml full cream milk
2 egg yolks
1 tsp vanilla essence
¼ cup caster sugar
Pinch ground cinnamon

Preheat oven to 200°C. Whisk eggs, milk and flours together. In a small saucepan put the sugar, vanilla essence, cinnamon and 1 tbsp water. Bring to the boil and whisk gently. Pour over the flour mix and heat until it thickens to coat the back of a spoon. Remove from heat and refrigerate.

Using a 6cm cutter, cut out 9 circles of the puff pastry on a floured surface. Grease a muffin pan and place the pastry rounds into each of the indentations. Ensure that the pastry is flush with the sides of the tin.

Spoon the cooled custard into the pastry cups allowing a small gap from surface for expansion of the custard. Bake in oven for 15-20 mins then remove and let cool on a wire rack.

PRUNE & ALMOND CAKE

Serves 8
Prep 10 minutes
Cook 55 minutes

15 dried prunes, pitted
160g butter
160g caster sugar
3 eggs
2 cups ground almonds
1½ tsp vanilla essence
1½ cups self–raising flour
½ tsp baking powder
Extra pitted prunes and
    almonds for decoration

Preheat oven to 180°C.

Finely chop the prunes and set aside. Place butter and sugar in a bowl and cream together until light in colour. Add the eggs and beat well. Fold in the prunes, ground almonds, sifted flour, baking powder and vanilla essence.

Pour into a 20cm greased non-stick cake tin. Whole almonds and prunes can be sprinkled over the top for decoration (depending on modified diet requirements). Place cake on middle shelf and cook for about 45 – 55 mins. Test with a skewer; if it comes out clean it is ready.

Remove from oven and allow to cool on a tray. Serve with plum jam and cream.

Tips: **Cake can be portioned and frozen for a later time. ~ Other stone fruit can be used in place of the prunes.**

WELSH FRUIT BREAD (BARA BRITH)

Serves 12 slices/serves
Prep 20 minutes
Cook about 60 minutes

450g dried mixed fruit
250ml English breakfast tea,
    black (hot)
500g self-raising flour
2 tbsp marmalade
2 tsp mixed spice
7 tbsp soft brown sugar
100g melted butter
2 free range eggs beaten
1 tsp mixed ground spice
Honey to glaze

Lightly grease and line with baking paper 1 x 450g loaf tin. Soak the fruit and sugar in the hot milk-less tea overnight In a mixing bowl, stir together the flour and spice and marmalade until completely mixed together. Finally, add the beaten egg.

Preheat oven to 160°C.

Place the mix into the lined loaf tin and put on the middle shelf in the oven. Bake for 60 mins or until the top is golden brown. Remove from oven and glaze liberally with the honey.

Tips: **These keep 2 weeks in a sealed container or, if individually wrapped and left in a freezer, they can keep for several weeks. ~ They are ideal served cold with lashings of good butter or can be toasted with butter.**

SUPER SNACKS

Melted butter, simmering onion, garlic infusions—these super-creative snacks cover an array of cuisines, textures and tastes! From English pasties to Aussie fish and chips, Mediterranean meatballs to Japanese barbecue, these recipes will cure any craving—especially as they are easy to eat with your hands!

CHICKEN EMPANADAS

Serves 4
Prep 15 minutes
Cook 15-20 minutes

1 batch of sour cream pastry
    dough (see 'Basic recipes')
300g minced chicken thigh
    fillet
½ cup sweetcorn kernels,
    fresh or frozen
2 cloves garlic, minced
2 hardboiled eggs
    (see 'Basic recipes')
1 egg, beaten
½ Spanish onion fine diced
½ cup sliced mushrooms
2 tbsp extra virgin olive oil
3 tbsp finely chopped parsley
2 tsp sea salt flakes
1 tsp ground white pepper

Preheat oven to 200°C. Roll out pastry between 2 sheets of baking paper until a diameter of 3mm thickness, and refrigerate.

Heat the oil in a non-stick frying pan, and cook the onions slowly until translucent. Add the garlic and continue to cook. Remove the onion and garlic and set aside.

In the same pan add a dash more oil and cook the minced chicken thigh fillet until brown. Add the onion and garlic to the chicken and then the mushroom and corn. Continue until the mushrooms are cooked.

Add the chopped parsley, hard-boiled eggs and seasoning. Stir through until all combined. Allow to cool.

Divide the mixture into 4. Cut out the pastry into 10cm rounds. Place filling into centre, brush the edges with a beaten egg to help it bind. Fold the pastry in half and crimp around the edges.

Bake the pastries until golden brown, about 12-15 mins.

Tip: **Also great with pulled beef—see 'Basic recipes'.**

CHICKEN, SWEET POTATO & BEAN CAKES

Serves 10 cakes/2 per serve
Prep 45 minutes
Cook 45 minutes

½ cup diced sweet potato
2 tbsp olive oil
250g chicken breast diced skin off
200g drained cannellini beans (about ½ can)
½ finely chopped onion
1 clove garlic
½ tsp sea salt flakes
¼ tsp ground white pepper
½ tsp paprika
1 tbsp chopped flat leaf parsley
3 eggs whisked with a 1 tbsp milk (egg wash)
3 cups panko breadcrumbs or
3 cups of ground cornflakes

Coat the sweet potato in the olive oil and place on a tray. Bake at 180°C until sweet potato is cooked through.

In a food processor, mince the onion and garlic and then add the diced chicken and process until a minced texture forms. Add the drained cannellini beans and pulse once or twice to incorporate the beans to the chicken mix.

Place in a bowl and add the sweet potato, herbs and spices. Mix well. Form into 10 patties and freeze for 20 mins. Remove the patties and dip into the egg batter and then carefully place into the breadcrumbs or cornflakes to coat each one.

To cook, place on a baking tray spray with olive oil spray and bake in the preheated oven for about 20 mins or until the cakes are cooked through.

Tips: **Prior to cooking, the cakes can be flash frozen individually on a tray and then wrapped in cling film and placed in a snap sealed freezer bag. The cakes will keep for 3 months frozen.**

CORNISH PASTIE

Serves 4
Prep 30 minutes
Cook 45 minutes

125g chilled and diced butter
125g lard
500g plain flour, plus extra
Pinch salt
Splash of water
1 egg, beaten

Filling
400g lean beef, or lamb finely
  diced or minced
1 large onion, finely sliced
2 medium potatoes, peeled,
  thinly sliced
175g swedes, peeled,
  finely diced
2 tsp sea salt
1 tsp ground white pepper
1 tbsp chopped parsley
  and thyme

Rub the butter and lard into the flour with a pinch of salt using your fingertips or a food processor, then blend in 6 tbsp of cold water to make a firm dough. Cut equally into 4, then chill for 20 mins.

Heat oven to 200°C. Mix together the filling ingredients with 1 teaspoon of salt. Roll out each piece of dough on a lightly floured surface until large enough to make one round, about 15cm across—using a plate to trim to shape.

Firmly pack a quarter of the filling along the centre of each round, leaving a margin at each end. Brush the pastry all the way round the edge with beaten egg.

Carefully draw up both sides so that they meet at the top, then pinch them together to seal. Lift onto a non-stick baking tray and brush with the remaining egg to glaze.

Bake for 10 mins, then lower oven to 180°C and cook for 45 mins until golden. Serve warm.

Story: The Cornish pasty is the ultimate hand-held food. This ancient recipe stems back to Cornish miners—their wives would bake the pasties with one half savoury and the other sweet, with a letter on the sweet end. The miners would eat the savoury half, continue to work and have the sweet end for a treat later on.

Tips: **Any combination of meats, vegetables and spices can be used, and any kind of pastry. ~ The pastry in this recipe is the traditional style and is packed with animal fat which is a good source of energy for older people. ~ Shop bought puff pastry sheets or shortcrust pastry are also worth trying. ~ If not using lard, just use a total of 250g of butter.**

FISH AND CHIPS

Serves 2
Prep 40 minutes
Cook 15 minutes

Fish

250g flathead fillets skin off,
   bones removed (or any firm
   white fish)
3 tbsp plain flour
Zest of ½ lemon
½ tbsp parsley flakes
¼ tsp ground paprika
1 free range egg beaten
1 cup fine white breadcrumbs
   or panko Japanese
   breadcrumbs
2 tbsp sesame seeds
Sea salt flakes and ground
   white pepper to taste

Chips

2 russet or sebago potatoes,
   peeled and cut into 1.5 cm
   thick chips
Rice bran oil to fry

Cut the fish into 2cm-thick finger-like strips. In a small bowl, add the flour and paprika and add a little sea salt and ground white pepper. In a separate bowl, add the egg and season this also, in a third bowl place the bread crumbs and lemon zest, sesame seeds and parsley.

Dip the fish strips first in the flour, then the egg and then in the breadcrumbs. Remove from crumbs and rest for 30 mins in refrigerator. Repeat process until all the fish is coated.

Place the potato chips in a large saucepan of water and bring to boil over a high heat. Cook for 10 mins or until they are just cooked. Drain well and lay on a tray to cool.

Fill a deep fryer or a saucepan to one third with rice bran oil and heat to 180°C or until a cube of bread turns brown in 15 secs when immersed. Deep fry the chips in 2 batches until golden brown, carefully remove with a slotted spoon, lay on paper towels and keep warm.

Add more oil and bring the temperature up to 180°C. Slowly lower the fish into the oil and cook for 3-4 mins or until golden brown and cooked through.

Serve immediately with the chips and a wedge of lemon, cucumber sticks and a cherry tomato salad.

Tips: **Be careful using the oil and do not attempt to move it while hot or leave it unattended. The fish will take about 10 mins. Remove the fish and turn it over to coat with melted better. Cook for another 5 mins. ~ Alternatively, the chips can be sprayed with olive oil spray and baked in the oven for 15 mins or until golden brown.**

GRILLED CHICKEN & FIG SALAD WITH SWEET POTATO

Serves 2
Prep 10 minutes
Cook 30 minutes

1 chicken breast
½ sweet potato peeled and
    cut into large dice
1 sprig rosemary
2 cloves garlic, crushed
2 figs
2 tbsp olive oil
1 tbsp honey
½ tbsp picked leaf parsley

Preheat oven to 180°C.

Drizzle the sweet potato with a little olive oil. Add sea salt, rosemary and the garlic. Place in the oven at 180°C and cook until the sweet potato is golden and softened slightly. Remove and allow to cool.

Brush chicken breast with a little olive oil, and season with sea salt flakes and ground black pepper. Cook the chicken on a hot barbecue for 5 mins on each side until cooked through. Set aside.

Heat the lemon juice and the honey in a small saucepan, cut the chicken into large chunks, cut the figs in half and add the sweet potato. Arrange nicely onto 2 plates and drizzle with the honey glaze.

Tip: **This is also great with the roasted baby chats, roasted button mushrooms and green beans.**

GRILLED LAMB CUTLETS, ASPARAGUS, KIPFLER POTATOES & MUSHROOMS

Serves 2
Prep 10 minutes
Cook 14 minutes

4 medium kipfler potatoes,
  scrubbed
4 lamb cutlets—ask butcher
to French trim the bones
6 button mushrooms
6 asparagus spears
1 garlic clove, crushed
1 rosemary sprig
Sea salt to taste
Ground black pepper to taste
3 tbsp extra virgin olive oil

Cook the kipfler potatoes in salted water until cooked through. Allow to cool.

Trim the end off of the asparagus spears and cook for 2 mins in simmering salted water. Remove and refresh under cold running water. Cut the kipfler potatoes in half lengthways.

Heat a frying pan with 2 tbsp of extra virgin olive oil , add the four cutlets and the potatoes, garlic and rosemary sprig and cook until cutlets are browned nicely (2 mins each side)

Turn cutlets and potatoes over and add a little more virgin olive oil. Season with sea salt and ground black pepper and add the button mushrooms. Cook on a low heat until mushrooms and cutlets are cooked, and finally add the asparagus spears to warm through.

Remove the cutlets and arrange equal amounts of the vegetables and potatoes on both plates. If required, the bone can be removed for ease of eating.

Tip: **The lamb is best served medium as it retains its moisture.**

GRILLED LAMB MEATBALLS

Serves 4
Prep 10 minutes
Cook 15 minutes

300g lean lamb mince
150g fine burghul wheat
soaked in cold water for
   10 mins, drained and
   squeezed dry
100g onions sliced
100g pork fat minced or
chopped fine (lamb fat
   can be used)
100g mozzarella ball diced
   into 5mm cubes
50g dried mint
2 tbsp flat leaf parsley
3 tsp sea salt flakes
2 tsp freshly ground
   white pepper

Place the lamb, burghul, and onions in a mixing bowl and knead together, then add the lamb/pork fat and mix this in well. Sprinkle in the salt, pepper, dried mint and parsley and knead the mixture.

Divide the mixture into even sized balls (2 bites each size). Poke a hole in the meatball with your finger and insert a couple of pieces of the mozzarella and reform into rounds. Wet your hands to make rolling easier.

When all the meat and cheese has been formed into balls place the meatballs on a barbecue and grill for 10-15 mins until browned evenly all over.

Tip: **Great served with roasted baby chat potatoes, cherry tomatoes and cucumber wedges.**

BUBBLE & SQUEAK CAKES WITH BACON

Serves 2
Prep 10 minutes
Cook 25 minutes

2 large floury potatoes,
   desiree or maris piper
1 tbsp cream
2 tbsp butter
1 cup shredded savoy
   cabbage
1 cup grated cheddar cheese
1 tsp sea salt flakes
½ tsp ground white pepper
½ tbsp chopped flat leaf
   parsley
2 rashers bacon, small diced
1 hard-boiled egg chopped
Extra virgin olive oil to
   cook cakes

Peel the potatoes and cut into equal sizes and cook in simmering salted water for 15 mins or until cooked.

Melt 1 tbsp of butter in a frying pan, cook the bacon until brown and remove, retaining the oil. Cook the cabbage in the bacon oil and butter until soft.

Drain the cooked potatoes and place in saucepan with the cream and 1 tbsp of butter and mash. Season with the salt and pepper, then add the cabbage, chopped egg, parsley and bacon, mixing carefully. Form into 4 large cakes.

In a non-stick frying pan heat 3 tbsp of olive oil. Pan-fry the cakes on both sides until crisp and golden brown then place on absorbent paper to remove any excess oil, and serve.

Tips: **Bacon can be omitted and cooked in thick cubes and served with cakes. ~ Egg can also be served in wedges separately. ~ This mix is also ideal to fill cooked potato skins. ~ Ham can also be used in place of bacon.**

JAPANESE BARBECUE PORK

Serves makes 4 skewers
Prep 5 minutes
Cook 8-10 minutes

250g diced pork fillet cut into
   3cm dice
1 Spanish onion
1 red capsicum
4 tbsp teriyaki sauce
1 tsp grated ginger
1 tsp sea salt flakes
½ tsp ground white pepper
1 tsp lime zest
2 tsp chopped coriander
Rice bran oil; or vegetable oil
   to cook
4 bamboo skewers
   soaked in water

Cut the Spanish onion and red capsicum into 3cm square dice.

Soak skewers in water for 1 hour, and then alternately skewer pork, onion and capsicum onto 4 skewers (20 cm). Mix the teriyaki sauce with ginger, lime zest and salt and pepper and pour over the skewers. Cover and refrigerate for 2 hours.

Preheat barbecue and remove skewers from refrigerator. Turn and recoat with the marinade. Place on lightly oiled hotplate and cook on all sides for about 1 minute each side, or until the pork is cooked through. Remove from barbecue and sprinkle with chopped coriander.

This is ideally served with rice cakes or a green salad or try cubing cucumber and pickling with a little white wine vinegar and a dash of soy sauce.

Tips: **Can be served with barbecue sauce to dip, grated carrot and wedges of iceberg. ~ This recipe can be frozen before cooking, and kept for up to 3 months. ~ The meat can also be taken off the skewer and put into a wrap with hummus as a sandwich filling.**

SALMON BURGERS

Serves 4
Prep 10 minutes (+ 2hrs rest)
Cook 10 minutes

400g can pink salmon,
  drained
1 cup ricotta cheese
½ cup chopped shallots
(spring onions)
2 tbsp chopped parsley
1 zucchini, grated finely
1 medium tomato
½ tbsp lemon juice
1 tsp sea salt flakes
½ tsp ground white pepper
1 free range egg
4 soft buns

Coating
1 egg & 100ml cream beaten
  to coat burger
1 cup flour
1 cup fresh white
  breadcrumbs (remove
  crust from 6 slices bread
  and process until crumbs
  in a food processor)
2 tbsp sesame seeds
  (optional)

Place drained salmon, egg, grated zucchini, ricotta, spring onions, lemon juice and seasoning in a bowl with the parsley and mix by hand and form into 4 patties.

Mix the egg and cream in a small bowl and season with a little salt and pepper. Place the breadcrumbs and the sesame seeds into another small bowl.

Dip the burgers one by one in the flour, then the egg mix, then the breadcrumbs. Once all are coated, leave in refrigerator to firm for a few hours.

Heat a little extra virgin olive oil in a non-stick frying pan and cook the burgers on each side until golden brown in colour. Serve in a soft bun with sliced tomato.

*Tip: **These fritters are best served hot with a squeeze of fresh lemon juice.***

KOREAN STYLE HAMBURGER

Serves 4
Prep 10 minutes
Cook 10 minutes

125g lean beef, minced
125g lean pork, minced
2 garlic cloves, crushed
1 spring onion, finely sliced
60g white bread crumbs
1 tbsp chopped flat leaf
   parsley
1 tsp sesame seeds
2 tsp sesame seed oil
1 tsp sea salt flakes
½ tsp ground white pepper
½ tbsp sugar

In a bowl combine the meat with the rest of the ingredients and mix well. Shape the mixture into 6 flat patties. Grill the hamburger over hot coals on a barbecue for 10 mins, turning once.

Tips: **Can also be rolled into 12 balls and cooked in an oven, or on 4 skewers on barbecue. ~ Great served with a nice condiment and a soft roll with melted cheese.**

LAMB KOFTA

Serves 4
Prep 5 minutes
Cook 5-10 minutes

250g lamb mince
75g crumbled feta cheese
1/4 small onion
½ clove garlic
2 tsp chopped mint
1 tsp cumin
½ tbsp chopped flat leaf
   parsley
½ tsp mild paprika
¼ tsp ground coriander
Pinch of ginger
½ tsp sea salt
¼ tsp ground white pepper

Place mince, onion, garlic, mint, parsley, paprika, feta, ginger, cumin and coriander in a bowl. Mix to combine.

Divide lamb mixture into 4 x 8cm-long sausages. Thread 1 sausage onto each skewer. Place on a large baking tray and cover. Refrigerate for 20 mins or until firm.

Heat an oiled barbecued plate on high. Add the kofta and reduce heat to low. Cook, turning occasionally, for 10 mins or until cooked through. Transfer to a large baking tray. Cover with foil and rest for 5 mins.

Tips: **Use either beef or pork mince for an alternative. ~ Great with hummus and yoghurt for a dip. ~ Serve with carrot strips and cucumber batons, cheese cubes.**

PAN FRIED SALMON, SWEET POTATO, ASPARAGUS & TOMATO

Serves 2
Prep 5 minutes
Cook 25 minutes

2 x 110g salmon steaks,
   skinned, deboned
   (cut in half)
6 asparagus spears
½ medium sized sweet
   potato, peeled and
   diced 3cm
6 grape tomatoes
Extra virgin olive oil
Sea salt and ground white
   pepper
Lemon to serve

Heat oven to 180°C and place the sweet potato on baking paper on a non-stick baking tray and drizzle with a little olive oil and salt and pepper.

Bake in oven for 10 mins, then add the four pieces of salmon. Season salmon with a little sea salt and bake in oven for 5 mins then remove the tray from the oven.

Add the asparagus and place the sweet potato, salmon and asparagus back in the oven. Remove after 8 mins and the salmon should be almost cooked through.

Remove and place all items onto 2 plates, adding the tomatoes whole.

Serve with a wedge of lemon.

Tip: **Any nice firm piece of fish can be substituted for salmon, just be careful to remove the bones.**

PIZZA MARGHERITA

Serves 2 pizzas/4 serves
Prep 10 minutes if
not making base
Cook 6-12 minutes

Pizza dough (see 'Basic
  recipes') or purchase a
  30cm pizza base
4 roma tomatoes
8 fresh basil leaves
2 crushed garlic cloves
2 tbsp passata (available in
  supermarkets in a jar or
  use pizza tomato base
  sauce)
3 tbsp extra virgin olive oil
200g ball mozzarella ball
  chopped
Sea salt flakes
Ground black pepper to taste

Make the pizza base according to basic recipe or place pre-bought 30cm base on a baking sheet, pre-heat oven to 200°C.

Take the core and seeds out of the tomatoes and chop finely in a food processor (or on a chopping board) with 4 basil leaves. Add to the passata and garlic.

Add 2 tbsp of olive oil to the tomato base and spread the mix evenly over the 30cm round pizza base. Make sure the sauce reaches the rim of the pizza. Scatter mozzarella over the top of the base, drizzle with a little more olive oil and sprinkle with sea salt flakes.

Place in the hot oven and cook for approximately 6-12 mins or until the base is golden and the cheese has colour on top. Remove and sprinkle the basil leaves over and drizzle with more oil and cracked black pepper.

Cut into wedges and serve. Ideal with tomato wedges, cucumber sticks and baby bocconcini salad. A great snack food for eating with fingers.

Tips: **Any variety of toppings can be added to this pizza ~ For something different, fold in half once cooked and allow to cool slightly and then cut into wedges (this is called calzone).**

SARDINE FRITTERS

Serves 2
Prep 5 minutes
Cook 15 minutes

1 can of good-quality oil-
    packed sardines, drained
    and chopped
1 large egg
1 cloves garlic, finely chopped
¼ bunch parsley leaves,
    finely chopped plus extra,
    for garnish
1 tbsp chopped mild chillies
    cup fresh breadcrumbs
1 tbsp grated parmesan
    cheese
 Extra-virgin olive oil, to
    fill a deep pot no more
    than halfway
Freshly ground black pepper
Sea salt to taste
Lemon halves

In a medium-sized mixing bowl, combine the canned sardine, eggs, garlic, parsley, chilli, bread crumbs and cheese. Stir lightly with a wooden spoon, being careful not to mash mixture. Set the fish mixture aside.

Fill a deep pot no more than halfway full with the olive oil. Heat over a medium flame until the temperature reaches 200°C (the oil should remain at or around this temperature throughout the frying process.)

Using a spoon, make fritters into semi-balls. When the oil reaches temperature, gently drop the fish balls into the hot oil. Be careful not to splatter the oil. Fry each fritter to a golden brown, about 2 mins.

Carefully remove the cooked fritters with a slotted spoon and reserve on a serving dish. Repeat until all of the fish mixture has been used.

SOUTHERN FRIED CHICKEN

Serves 4
Prep 10 minutes
Cook 15 minutes

4 pieces chicken thigh fillet
  with skin on (about 1kg)
2 tsp paprika
2 eggs lightly beaten
170g fine breadcrumbs or
  panko crumbs
¼ tsp thyme
1 clove garlic chopped fine
1 tsp sea salt flakes
½ tbsp chopped parsley
  flakes
Olive oil to cook

Cut the thigh fillets into 2 pieces and rub all the pieces well with the seasoning. Dip all the pieces into the beaten egg and carefully coat in the panko breadcrumbs.

In a large deep frying pan, heat olive oil and carefully place the chicken pieces in, browning each side. Carefully remove when brown on both sides and place on a clean baking tray in a preheated oven 180°C for 15 mins or until they are cooked.

Serve with green beans and roasted small potatoes

SCOTCH EGGS

Serves 3
Prep 15 minutes
Cook 8-10 minutes

4 eggs
½ onion chopped
1 garlic clove chopped
1 small mild chilli deseeded
    and chopped (optional)
1 tbsp chopped parsley
250g good quality pork
    sausage meat
½ tsp sea salt
¼ tsp white ground pepper

Coating station
Plain flour, to dust
1 egg and 2 tbsp cream
    mixed to make egg wash
Breadcrumbs
Oil to fry

Place the plain flour on a plate. Place 3 eggs in a saucepan of cold water and slowly bring to the boil. Boil eggs for 12 mins.

Drain and set aside to cool completely. Peel and dust the eggs in a little flour so the surface is dry.

Process the onion, garlic, chilli and herbs in a food processor. Add the sausage meat and process until it is chopped even finer and the ingredients are well combined. Add the remaining egg and process until the mixture comes together.

Divide the mixture into 3 even portions. Mould a portion in the cup of your hand. Place a hard-boiled egg into the 'cup' and shape the meat around to enclose. Roll it to smooth the surface.

Place flour in a bowl, egg wash in a spare bowl and breadcrumbs in another bowl. Roll the sausage meat egg pieces in flour, then the egg wash and finally the breadcrumbs. Ensuring they are completely covered in breadcrumbs and set aside. Repeat with the other 2 eggs.

Line a plate with a paper towel. When you have assembled all of the Scotch eggs, deep fry them a few at a time in deep oil over a medium heat for at least 10 mins, making sure they are evenly browned all over. Drain on the lined plate.

JUST DESSERTS

Who said desserts are bad for you? Enjoyable, enticing sweets made easy to eat—it's the icing on the cake, the cherry on the top, the delicate chocolate truffle in your hand! For a lot of older people, sweet foods are especially popular. These desserts are designed to satisfy the guilty pleasure without the guilt!

CHOCOLATE CHEESECAKE BROWNIE

Serves makes
14 slices/serves
Prep 10 minutes
Cook 50 minutes

190g melted butter
¼ cup cocoa powder sifted
1 cup caster sugar
2 free range eggs
1 cup plain flour, sifted

Cheesecake
285g cream cheese
4½ tbsp caster sugar
2 eggs
Cocoa powder, for dusting

Preheat oven to 160°C, mix the cocoa, sugar, melted butter and eggs in a bowl until smooth. Spoon mix into a 20cm square slice tin greased and lined with baking paper.

To make the cheesecake, process the cheese, eggs and sugar in a food processor until smooth. Dollop the cheesecake mix on top of the chocolate mixture and swirl with a knife.

Bake for 45-50 mins or until the cake is set. Cool in the tin, remove and dust liberally with cocoa powder. Cut into squares.

Tips: **Keeps well refrigerated for a couple of days. ~ It can also be frozen in slices. ~ Try adding berries and/ or sultanas.**

CHOCOLATE TRUFFLES

Serves 8
Prep 10 minutes

75g good dark chocolate
80g unsalted butter
1½ cups cream
2 tbsp milk powder
100g ground almonds
Good cocoa powder for
   dusting

Place chocolate, butter and cream in a saucepan and add milk powder and stir until melted.

Fold in the ground almonds and pour mixture into a lined 20cm square cake tin. Refrigerate overnight then cut into small squares and dust with cocoa powder.

Tips: **As an alternative, soak 100g sultanas in whiskey, bring to simmer in small pan and allow to steep, then add to the truffles with the ground almonds for a decadent snack.**

MAGGIE BEER'S GINGER COCONUT SLICE

Serves 36 pieces/18 serves
Prep 25 mins
(+ setting time in the fridge)

Base
1½ cups almond meal
½ cup shredded coconut
45ml coconut oil, melted
⅓ cup dates, soaked
1 tbsp honey

Topping
1 cup soaked cashews
¼ cup almond milk
1½ tbsp fresh grated ginger
Juice of ½ lemon
½ teaspoon lemon zest
Pinch salt
1 tsp vanilla
¼ cup honey
¼ cup coconut oil

Grease and line a 20x28cm slice tin.

Base

Place all ingredients in a food processor and pulse together. Press into the lined tin and set in the fridge for about 1 hour or until firm.

Topping

Place all ingredients (except coconut oil) into the food processor and blend until smooth. Add coconut oil, combine and pour evenly on top of the cake base (you can sprinkle with chia seeds, coconut or grated nuts). Set in the fridge until firm.

Slide onto a board and cut into 36 pieces.

Maggie Beer assisted HammondCare in the appointment of executive chef Peter Morgan-Jones and continues to be an advocate for aged care food through the Maggie Beer Foundation.

DUKE OF DEVONSHIRE'S NUT BISCUITS

Serves 8 biscuits, 4 serves
Prep 5 minutes
Cook 15 minutes

8 tbsp plain flour
4 tbsp castor sugar
2 free range egg yolks
130ml milk
120g butter
50g ground fresh almonds
Chocolate nut spread
    e.g. Nutella

Preheat oven to 160 °C. Rub the butter thoroughly through the flour, then add sugar and ground almonds. Mix well together. Then add the milk and egg yolks.

Roll biscuit batter to about 7mm in thickness and cut into rounds of about 6-7cm in diameter. Bake in oven for about 15 mins or until the biscuits are a pale gold colour.

Allow to cool and spread each half liberally with a smooth nut spread and sandwich the halves together.

Tips: **Any nut or chocolate filling can be added, or they can be eaten plain. ~ This has been adapted from a 17th century recipe.**

FLOURLESS CHOCOLATE CAKES

Serves–makes 12
Prep 10 minutes
Cook 30 minutes

180g chopped butter
220g dark chocolate
1¼ cups caster sugar
¾ cup almond meal
100g sultanas (soaked in hot
 black tea and drained)
1 cup cocoa powder
5 eggs

Preheat oven to 140°C. Place butter, sugar and chocolate in a small saucepan.

Heat on low until the chocolate has melted and has no lumps. Place the drained sultanas, almond meal and cocoa into a bowl and mix in the chocolate mixture. Add eggs gradually until well combined.

Grease a muffin tin (with 12 x ½ cup capacity non-stick tin). Spoon in the mixture and bake in middle of oven for about 30 mins or until firm to touch. Allow to cool in tin and serve with whipped cream.

Tip: **Freezes well.**

For some tasty modified dessert ideas see our
'Proudly modified' section.

LIME YOGHURT CAKE

Serves 8
Prep 15 minutes
Cook 45 minutes

125g butter
1 cup caster sugar
2 free range eggs, beaten
½ cup almond meal
1 cup Greek yoghurt
3 tbsp lime juice
1 tbsp lime rind
2 ½ cups self-raising flour
½ tsp baking soda

Syrup
1/3 cup caster sugar
½ cup water
3 tbsp lime juice
Rind of 1 lime cut into thin
    strips

Place butter and sugar in bowl or kitchen mixer and beat until pale and creamy, add eggs slowly and beat well. Stir in yoghurt, almond meal, lime juice and rind, flour and baking soda so they combine with the butter and eggs.

Spoon mixture into a greased, lined 23cm round cake tin and bake in preheated oven at 170°C for 45 mins or until the cake is cooked when tested with a skewer.

To make syrup combine all ingredients in a small pan, simmer until the sugar has dissolved.

When cake comes out of oven, reheat the syrup until simmering and pour hot over the hot cake. Allow to cool in the cake tin.

Tips: **This cake is ideal served with a dollop of yoghurt. ~ It's also nice to add sliced apple to the cake mixture before cooking. ~ An optional topping (pictured) is chopped pistachio, mint and lime/lemon slices poached in syrup.**

ROASTED PEACHES & CREAM POPSICLES

Serves 6 popsicles
–2 per serve
Prep 10 minutes
Cook 35 minutes

120g peaches, peeled and
   de-stoned, cut into eights
120ml milk
1 tbsp milk powder
1 tbsp brown sugar
½ tsp cinnamon
160ml Greek yoghurt
5 scoops Shape It gel powder

Preheat oven to 180°C, toss peaches in cinnamon and brown sugar, place on a tray lined with baking paper and roast for 20-30 mins until caramelised.

Chop peaches roughly, or if making for a modified diet, blend in a food processor until smooth. Pass through a sieve to remove any lumps.

In a small saucepan, heat milk, milk powder and Shape-it gel powder, simmer for 2 mins, add in peaches and yoghurt. Stir to combine.

Pour into popsicle moulds, tap to remove bubbles and freeze until set.

NOTE: The popsicles pictured are those for a soft diet. Please ensure you strain/sieve the mixture before setting, if you are on a pureed or minced diet.

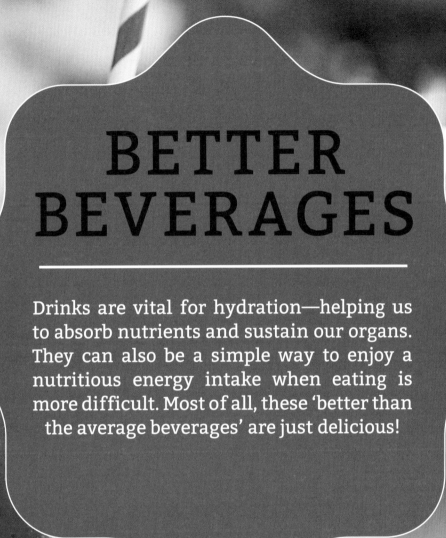

BETTER BEVERAGES

Drinks are vital for hydration—helping us to absorb nutrients and sustain our organs. They can also be a simple way to enjoy a nutritious energy intake when eating is more difficult. Most of all, these 'better than the average beverages' are just delicious!

APPLE BRAN SMOOTHIE

Serves 2
Prep 5 minutes

½ cup apple puree
½ cup natural yoghurt
1 tbsp flax meal
1 wheat biscuit (Weetbix)
½ cup apple juice
4 cubes of ice

Add all ingredients to a blender. Blend for 1-2 mins until all ingredients are combined. Serve immediately.

For thickened drinks, strain and thicken using thickening powder to manufacturer's instructions.

R S M P T Th1 Th2 Th3

WATERMELON & ALMOND SMOOTHIE

Serves 2
Prep 5 minutes

2 cups diced seedless watermelon
⅓ cup natural yoghurt
2 tbsp almond meal
½ cup high protein milk
1 scoop vanilla ice-cream
1 tsp honey

Blend all ingredients except ice-cream until smooth. When blended, add the ice-cream and pulse until frothy. Pass through a sieve before serving.

For thickened fluids, follow directions from thickener manufacturer.

R S M T Th1 Th2 Th3

ICED COFFEE

Serves 2
Prep 5 minutes

½ cup espresso coffee
2 tsp caster sugar
1 cup high protein milk
6 ice cubes
4 scoops vanilla ice-cream

Place coffee and sugar in a jug, stir until sugar has dissolved. Add high protein milk, stir to combine.

Divide ice and ice-cream into 2 glasses, top with coffee mixture and serve immediately.

For thickened fluids, follow directions from thickener manufacturer, omit ice cream and omit ice cubes or, they can be pre-thickened before freezing in cube trays.

GINGER ALE

Serves makes 1.5 litres
/6 serves
Prep 5 minutes
Cook 10 minutes

110g ginger, peeled and
   sliced
1 cups caster sugar
1 sprig of mint
1/4 cup freshly squeezed
   lemon juice
1.5 litres water

Place all ingredients in a pan and simmer for 10 mins. Allow to cool and carefully strain into bottles, seal and refrigerate. Serve over ice with a sprig of mint.

For thickened fluids, follow directions from the thickener manufacturer and omit ice cubes, or they can be prethickened before freezing in ice cube trays.

CEYLON TEA PUNCH

Serves 3 cups
Prep 10 minutes
Chilling 30 minutes

2 tsp good quality Ceylon tea
   leaves
1¼ cup boiling water
½ cup lime juice
¼ cup lemon juice
110g soft brown sugar
1 lemon, thinly sliced
2 mint sprigs

Place the tea in a large jug and infuse with boiling water. After 5 mins, strain and discard the strained tea-leaves. Place sugar, lime juice and lemon juice and slices and mint into the jug and stir until sugar has dissolved. Allow to chill covered in the refrigerator.

To serve strain the mint and lemon and pour in glass with ice cubes.

For thickened drinks, strain and thicken using thickening powder to manufacturer's instructions. Please refer to 'Contacts and resources' for thickener stockists.

Tips: **To make this an indulgent alcoholic, special occasion, tea punch—add 1½ cups dry vermouth and 3 tbsp of brandy. ~ This is great on a hot, balmy day!**

CHOCOLATE, BANANA & ALMOND SMOOTHIE

Serves 2
Prep 5 minutes

1 large banana or 2 small, frozen
200ml chilled high protein milk
1 tbsp almond butter
1 tsp cocoa powder
½ tsp maple syrup
1 tsp LSA (see tips)

In a blender combine frozen banana, milk, almond butter, cacao, maple syrup and LSA. Blend on high for 1 minute. Pour into a glass and serve. For thickened drinks, strain and thicken using thickening powder to manufacturer's instructions.

Tips: **Ensure you strain before serving for pureed diet. ~ Try and use frozen fruit for smoothies, it makes them icy cold and gives a thicker consistency. ~ When freezing bananas, make sure that you peel them first, slice into thirds and place into a zip lock bag. This will make them easier to blend. ~ LSA is a high protein mixture of ground linseed, sunflower seeds and almonds and is available in the health food section of the supermarket.**

SPICED MANGO LASSI

Serves 2
Prep 5 minutes

1 mango, chopped
2 tbsp natural yoghurt
½ cup high protein milk
1 tsp honey
¼ tsp ground cinnamon
¼ tsp ground cardamom

Add diced mango, yoghurt, milk, honey, cinnamon and cardamom to a blender. Blend until smooth, and as an option, blend with ice if you prefer. Pass through a sieve before serving. Enjoy!

For thickened fluids, follow directions from thickener manufacturer and omit ice cubes or they can be pre-thickened before freezing in ice cube trays.

STRAWBERRY SMOOTHIE

Serves 2
Prep 5 minutes

1 cup chilled high protein
 milk
1 cup frozen strawberries
 (about 6)
½ cup apple juice
1 tbsp natural yoghurt
1 tsp flax meal

Add strawberries, milk, apple juice, yoghurt and flax meal to a high powered blender. Blend for 1-2 min or until smooth. Pass through a sieve before serving.

For thickened fluids, add thickener and follow manufacturer's instructions.

Tips: **Flax meal or ground flax seed is available in general supermarkets. ~ Strawberries can be purchased snap frozen from the freezer section, or alternatively freeze your own by washing, hulling and sealing in zip lock bags in the freezer.**

PROUDLY MODIFIED

Swallowing difficulties can add to the challenge of taking in essential nutrients and enjoying food. It's even harder for people who are also uncomfortable with cutlery. But these recipes for marvellously modified food help bring back dignity and freedom. Not only are they appetising and beautifully presented, but suitable for a range of diets and, amazingly, able to be eaten by hand.

Most of these recipes are designed to be part of a meal such as a protein, vegetable, or fruit component. Many use a new, specially designed gel powder called Shape It. Our scoop measurement is 1 gram. Also many utilise special food moulds—see 'Contacts and resources'

APPLE AND STRAWBERRY BIRCHER MUESLI SQUARES

Serves 2
Prep 15 minutes
Cook 2 minutes

1 cup instant oats
1 tbsp almond meal
1 tbsp milk powder
Pinch of cinnamon
Pinch of nutmeg
½ granny smith apple
2 hulled strawberries
1 cup apple juice
½ a lemon, juiced
1 tbsp honey
½ cup yoghurt
8 (1g) scoops Shape-it gel
  powder

Grind the oats in a coffee grinder and transfer to a medium bowl. Add almond meal, milk powder, cinnamon and nutmeg. In a food processor, combine the apple (skin on, cut into thirds), strawberry, lemon and apple juice and blend.

Pass the liquid through a sieve to strain; you should be left with 250ml of liquid. Transfer to a small saucepan and add honey, bring to a simmer. Add 5 level scoops of the gelling powder to the liquid, stir with a metal spoon, simmer for 2 mins.

Add yoghurt to liquid, whisking it in. Pour the liquid over the oats mixture, stir to combine. Line a small container with baking paper, pour the mixture in, cover with cling wrap and refrigerate until set.

Turn out onto a chopping board, cut into squares and serve.

Tips: **Can be served with modified fruit salad, and/or yoghurt cubes. ~ Serve at room temperature.**

3 CHEESE PANNA COTTA

Serves 3
Prep 5 minutes
Cook 2 minutes

100ml cream
50ml milk
1 tbsp milk powder
15g parmesan
15g cheddar
15g mozzarella
3 (1g) scoops Shape It gel
    powder
Pinch of paprika
Salt and pepper

Add cream, milk, milk powder, parmesan, cheddar, mozzarella, gel powder, paprika, salt and pepper in a small saucepan. Bring to a simmer. Stir for 2 mins.

Remove from heat, pour into sprayed moulds and refrigerate until set.

Tip: **Serve at room temperature.**

BAKED RICOTTA

Serves 6 serves
Prep 10 minutes
Cook 30 minutes

400g smooth ricotta
2 eggs
⅓ cup grated parmesan
Salt and white pepper
Paprika
Extra virgin olive oil spray

Preheat oven to 150°C.

Grease a 20cm enamel pie dish with the spray oil, line with baking paper, spray again and sprinkle with paprika.

In a food processor, combine ricotta, eggs, parmesan and salt and pepper. Blend until smooth. Pour into the pie dish, smooth and sprinkle with extra paprika.

Cover with baking paper, sealing the top of the ricotta mix and bake for 30 mins. Turn off the oven and allow to cool. Put in refrigerator, cut any crusts or hard edges off before serving.

Tips: **We love Australian olive oil! ~ Serve at room temperature. ~ Ensure no fluids from condensation remain on the plate—drain before serving.**

CREAMY BROCCOLI

Serves 4
Prep 5 minutes
Cook 7 minutes

125g broccoli
100ml cream
1 tbsp milk powder
Salt
White pepper
6½ (1g) scoops Shape It gel
powder

Wash broccoli well, cut into small pieces and cook in boiling salted water for 5 mins or until soft. Drain, blanch and drain again.

Add broccoli to a food processor with cream. Blend, scraping down the sides of the bowl with a spatula and re-blending 2-3 times until you have achieved a smooth consistency.

Transfer to a small saucepan. Season with salt and pepper, add milk powder and gel powder, stir to combine. Simmer over a low heat for 2 mins, stirring as needed.

Transfer to a non-stick container, lightly cover with cling wrap that is touching the surface of the puree and refrigerate until set.

Remove cling wrap, turn out onto a chopping board and portion. Serve.

Tip: **Serve at room temperature.**

CARROT PUREE PIECES

Serves 4
Prep 5 minutes
Cook 15 minutes

250g carrot
100ml cream
1 tbsp milk powder
Salt
White pepper
6½ (1g) scoops Shape It gel
   powder

Wash, peel and rewash carrots. Cut into small pieces and cook in boiling salted water for 10 mins or until soft. Drain, blanch and drain again.

Add carrot to a food processor with cream. Blend, scraping down the sides of the bowl with a spatula and re-blending 2-3 times until you have achieved a smooth consistency.

Transfer to a small saucepan and season with salt and pepper, add milk powder and gel powder, stir to combine.

Simmer over a low heat for 2 mins, stirring as needed.

Transfer to a non-stick container, cover loosely with cling wrap ensuring that it touches the surface of the puree and refrigerate until set.

Remove cling wrap, turn out onto a chopping board and portion. Serve.

Tip: **Serve at room temperature.**

SMOOTH VANILLA CARROTS

Serves 4
Prep 5 minutes
Cook 15 minutes

250g carrot
100ml cream
1 tbsp milk powder
½ tsp vanilla bean seeds
6½ (1g) scoops Shape It gel
   powder

Wash, peel and rewash carrots. Cut into small pieces and cook in boiling salted water for 10 mins or until soft. Drain, blanch and drain again.

Add carrot to a food processor with the cream. Blend, scraping down the sides of the bowl with a spatula and re-blending 2-3 times until you have achieved a smooth consistency.

Transfer to a small saucepan, and add milk powder, gel powder and vanilla, stir to combine. Simmer over a low heat for 2 mins, stirring as needed.

Transfer to a non-stick container, cover loosely with cling wrap ensuring that it is touching the top of the puree. Refrigerate until set.

Remove cling wrap, turn out onto a chopping board and portion. Serve.

Tip: **This is a delicious option for a sweet, healthy snack or dessert. ~ Serve at room temperature.**

CAULIFLOWER CHEESE PUREE SLICE

Serves 4
Prep 5 minutes
Cook 12 minutes

250g cauliflower, washed and
   cut into florets
100ml cream
1 pinch salt
White pepper
1 pinch nutmeg
1 tbsp milk powder
50g finely grated cheddar
6½ scoops of Shape It gel
   powder

Cook cauliflower in salted boiling water for about 10 mins, strain and refresh in cold water and strain again.

Add the cauliflower to a food processor with the cream and blend, scraping down the sides of the bowl with a spatula and re-blending 2-3 times until you have achieved a smooth consistency.

Transfer to a small saucepan and season with salt, pepper and nutmeg. Add the milk powder and gel powder, stir to combine. Cook over low heat for 2 mins, adding the cheese for the final 30 seconds.

Pour into pre-prepared non- stick container or mould, cover loosely with cling wrap ensuring that it is touching the top of the puree, chill in the fridge until set. Remove, cut into portions and serve.

Tip: **Serve at room temperature**

R   S   M   P   T   Th1   Th2   Th3

SWEET POTATO PUREE

Serves 4
Prep 5 minutes
Cook 15 minutes

250g sweet potato
100ml cream
1 tbsp milk powder
Salt
White pepper
6½ (1g) scoops Shape It gel
  powder

Wash, peel and rewash sweet potato. Cut into small pieces and cook in boiling salted water for 10 mins or until soft. Drain, blanch and drain again.

Add sweet potato to a food processor with cream. Blend, scraping down the sides of the bowl with a spatula and re-blending 2-3 times until you have achieved a smooth consistency

Transfer to a small saucepan. Season with salt and pepper, add milk powder and gel powder, stir to combine Simmer over a low heat for 2 mins, stirring as needed.

Transfer to a non-stick container, lightly cover with cling wrap that is touching the surface of the puree and refrigerate until set.

Remove cling wrap, turn out onto a chopping board and portion. Serve.

Tip: **Serve at room temperature.**

SPINACH & SWEET POTATO

Serves 4
Prep 20 minutes
Cook 12 minutes

200g sweet potato
80g frozen spinach (3 cubes)
100ml cream
1 tbsp milk powder
Salt
White pepper
6½ (1g) scoops Shape It gel
  powder

Wash, peel and rewash sweet potato. Cut into small pieces and cook in boiling salted water for 10 mins or until soft. Drain, blanch and drain again.

Add potato and spinach to a food processor with the cream. Blend, scraping down the sides of the bowl with a spatula and re-blending 2-3 times until you have achieved a smooth consistency.

Transfer to a small saucepan. Season with salt and pepper, add milk powder and gel powder, stir to combine. Simmer over a low heat for 2 mins, stirring as needed.

Transfer to a non-stick container, lightly cover with cling wrap that is touching the surface of the puree and refrigerate until set.

Remove cling wrap, turn out onto a chopping board and portion. Serve.

Tips: **To make into a pureed consistency, sieve before pouring into moulds. ~ Serve at room temperature.**

SALMON PUREE FILLETS

Serves 4
Prep 20 minutes
Cook 15 minutes

200g salmon fillet
200ml thickened cream
½ tsp salt
¼ tsp ground white pepper
1 egg white
1 pinch nutmeg
Extra virgin olive oil

Note: Sausage process is pictured on following pages.

Preheat the oven to 100°C, and ensure there are no bones, blood-lines or skin in the salmon. Dice and refrigerate.

Place the diced salmon, thickened cream, salt and pepper in a food processor and blend, scraping down the sides of the bowl with a spatula and re-blending 2-3 times until you have achieved a smooth consistency.

Pass the salmon mixture through a fine sieve and refrigerate.

Whisk the egg white in a clean, stainless steel bowl until it forms peaks. Using a metal spoon, fold the egg whites into the chilled salmon mixture.

Spray a fish fillet silicon mould with extra virgin olive oil and divide the mixture into 4 fish fillets. Tap the mould on the bench to raise air bubbles to the surface.

Spray the surface of the mould with more olive oil, and cover with baking paper. Cook in the oven for 12 mins.

Remove from the mould carefully and serve.

Tip: **Can be made into sausages by spooning mixture into cling wrap, rolling into a sausage shape, and poaching in water at 85°C for 8-10 mins, turning to ensure all sides are cooked. Remove with slotted spoon and allow to cool.**

PARSNIP & SWEET POTATO

Serves 4
Prep 5 minutes
Cook 15 minutes

150g parsnip
100g sweet potato
100ml cream
1 tbsp milk powder
Salt
White pepper
6½ (1g) scoops Shape It gel
   powder

Wash, peel and rewash parsnip and sweet potato. Cut into small pieces and cook in boiling salted water for 10 mins or until soft. Drain, blanch and drain again.

Add potato and parsnip to a food processor with cream. Blend, scraping down the sides of the bowl with a spatula and re-blending 2-3 times until you have achieved a smooth consistency.

Transfer to a small saucepan. Season with salt and pepper, add milk powder and gel powder, stir to combine. Simmer over a low heat for 2 mins, stirring as needed.

Transfer to a non-stick container, lightly cover with cling wrap that is touching the surface of the puree and refrigerate until set.

Remove cling wrap, turn out onto a chopping board and portion. Serve.

Tip: **Serve at room temperature.**

R S M T Th1 Th2 Th3

PUMPKIN & SEMOLINA FUDGE

Serves 4
Prep 5 minutes
Cook 15 minutes

250g pumpkin
⅓ cup full cream milk
1 tbsp milk powder
2 pinches ground cinnamon
1 tsp butter
Salt and ground white pepper
60g fine semolina
Extra virgin olive oil spray

Grease a square muffin pan, or any non-stick tray or container, with olive oil spray.

Wash, peel, rewash the pumpkin and cut into small cubes. In a medium saucepan, boil the pumpkin for 10-15 mins until tender.

Drain and add to a food processor. Blend, scraping down the sides of the bowl with a spatula and re-blending 2-3 times until you have achieved a smooth consistency.

In a small saucepan, combine milk, butter and cinnamon and bring to the boil. Reduce heat and slowly add the semolina. Reduce the heat and stir continuously with a wooden spoon for 3 mins, making sure there are no lumps, strain through a fine sieve.

Fold through pumpkin puree and mix until well combined, season to taste.

Using a silicon spatula, portion into the mini square muffin pan. If needed spread with spatula to flatten it out. Give the top a quick spray with oil, then cover with cling wrap. Allow to cool for 1.5 hours. Once cooled, turn out and serve.

Tips: **Can use takeaway containers. ~ Serve at room temperature. ~ Australian olive oil is our favourite!**

PEA PUREE

Serves 4
Prep 5 minutes
Cook 2 minutes

300g tin of mushy peas
100ml cream
1tbsp milk powder
6½ (1g) scoops Shape It gel
  powder
Salt and pepper

Add the peas to a food processor with a quarter of the cream. Blend, scraping down the sides of the bowl with a spatula and re-blending 2-3 times until you have achieved a smooth consistency. Add the rest of the cream in increments as you go.

Transfer to a small saucepan. Season with salt and pepper, add milk powder and gel powder, stir to combine. Simmer over a low heat for 2 mins, stirring as needed.

Transfer to a non-stick container, lightly cover with cling wrap that is touching the surface of the puree and refrigerate until set.

Remove cling wrap, turn out onto a chopping board and portion. Serve.

Tip: **Serve at room temperature.**

R S M P T Th1 Th2 Th3

HAM, MOZZARELLA & BUTTER BEAN SLICE

Serves 3
Prep 5 minutes
Cook 15 minutes

30g ham
75g of washed, drained,
    tinned butter beans
2 cups high protein milk
1 whole clove of garlic
Pinch of salt
2 pinches white pepper
1 sprig thyme
2 tbsp grated mozzarella
⅔ cup fine semolina
2 tbsp butter
1 tsp parsley flakes

Add ham, beans, thyme, milk, garlic, salt and pepper to a small saucepan and simmer for 5 mins, be careful not to boil. Remove the thyme and garlic and allow to cool slightly.

Strain the solids from the milk and add to a tall measuring jug with 100ml of the liquid. Blend carefully with a stick blender, adding more of the reserved liquid as necessary. Once you have a smooth texture, slowly add the rest of the milk and once completely blended, return to a clean saucepan.

Add the butter to the milk mixture, and bring back to a simmer. Slowly pour semolina into the liquid and stir continuously for 3 mins with a metal spoon. Gradually add parmesan and parsley to the mixture.

If the mixture is still lumpy, allow to cool slightly then and add to a food processor, scraping down the sides of the bowl with a spatula and re-blending 2-3 times until you have achieved a smooth consistency.

Spray a non-stick loaf pan with olive oil spray, pour mixture in, smoothing the top with the back of a metal spoon, cover with cling wrap and refrigerate until cool.

Serve at room temperature and cut into cubes.

Tip: **For another healthy alternative, use cannellini beans.**

PUREE CHICKEN DRUMSTICKS

Serves 3
Prep 15 minutes
Cook 15 minutes

200g chicken breast
200ml thickened cream
1 egg white
Salt
Ground white pepper
Extra virgin olive oil spray

Preheat oven to 100°C. Ensure that there are no bones, sinew and skin on the chicken, and dice into cubes.

Place the chicken, cream, salt and pepper into a food processor, scraping down the sides of the bowl with a spatula and re-blending 2-3 times until you have achieved a smooth consistency. Pass the chicken mixture through a fine sieve and refrigerate.

In a clean, stainless steel bowl, whisk the egg white until it forms peaks. Carefully fold the egg white into the chilled chicken mixture and spray a chicken drumstick silicon mould (see 'Contacts and resources' for stockists) with the olive oil spray.

Carefully fill 6 indentations with the mixture, tapping the mould on the bench to expel any air bubbles.

Spray the top of the mixture in the moulds with oil and cover with baking paper.

Bake at 100°C for 15 mins, remove and serve immediately.

CHICKEN FILLET SLICES

Serves 4
Prep 10 minutes
Cook 2 minutes

250g poached chicken thigh
fillet, chopped (see 'Basic
recipes')
150ml chicken stock
2 tbsp milk powder
Salt and pepper
Pinch nutmeg
8 (1g) scoops Shape It gel
powder

Add chicken stock to a small saucepan and bring to the boil

Add gel powder, salt and pepper, nutmeg and milk powder to the liquid, simmer for 1 minute. Add chopped chicken, continue to simmer for 1 more minute. Add to a food processor and blend until smooth.

Spray a silicone chicken mould, see resources for supplier, and portion blended chicken into 4 moulds.

Tap the moulds on the bench so that the mixture settles, then spray the top and cover with greaseproof paper. Refrigerate until set, slice and serve.

R S M T Th1 Th2 Th3

PULLED PORK TERRINE

Serves 3
Prep 10 minutes
Cook 2 minutes

250g pulled pork
150ml chicken stock
1 tbsp parsley flakes
8 (1g) scoops Shape It gel
  powder

In a small saucepan bring chicken stock to simmering point. Add the gel powder and simmer, stirring for 2 mins. Add pulled pork meat to the liquid and bring up to heat.

Remove from heat and blend in a food processor until smooth, stir in parsley flakes. Spray a small tin or container and add blended pork.

Refrigerate until set, remove, slice and serve at room temperature.

Tips: **Pulled pork can be cooked from the recipe in 'Basic recipes' or purchased from the supermarket. ~ Can be also used as a sandwich filling.**

R   S   M   T   Th1   Th2   Th3

APRICOT PUREE PIECES

Serves 4
Prep 5 minutes
Cook 2 minutes

200g apricot
150ml juice
Squeeze of lemon juice
5 (1g) scoops Shape It gel
  powder

Blend apricots and liquid along with lemon juice in a food processor until smooth. Transfer to a small saucepan and add gel powder, stir over heat for 2 mins.

Spray moulds, and then pour in mixture. (See 'Contacts and resource' for mould stockists.) Remove from moulds and serve.

Tips: **Serve alongside our fruit salad. ~ Serve at room temperature. ~ Ensure no fluids from condensation remain on the plate—drain before serving.**

PETE'S PUREE PEACHES

Serves 4
Prep 5 minutes
Cook 2 minutes

200g peaches, fresh or tinned
150ml liquid, from the tin or
  stock syrup
Squeeze of lemon juice
5 (1g) scoops Shape It gel
  powder

Blend peaches, lemon juice and liquid in a food processor until smooth. Transfer to a small saucepan and add gel powder, stir over heat for 2 mins.

Spray moulds (see 'Contacts and resources' for stockists). Remove from moulds and serve.

Tips: **With the right mould these will seem just like real peach pieces. ~ Serve alongside our fruit salad. ~ Serve at room temperature. ~Ensure no fluids from condensation remain on the plate—drain before serving.**

PERFECT PEAR PUREE

Serves 4
Prep 5 minutes
Cook 2 minutes

200g pear
150ml pear juice
Squeeze of lemon juice
6½ (1g) scoops of Shape It
 gel powder

Blend pears, lemon juice and pear juice in a food processor until smooth, scraping down the sides of the bowl with a spatula and re-blending 2-3 times until you have achieved a smooth consistency.

Transfer to a small saucepan and add gelling powder. Stir over heat for 2 mins. Spray moulds (see 'Contacts and resources' for stockists). Remove from moulds and serve.

Tips: **Can be served with yoghurt cubes. ~ Serve at room temperature. ~ Ensure no fluids from condensation remain on the plate/drain before serving.**

HAND-HELD PUREE WATERMELON

Serves 4
Prep 10 minutes
Cook 2 minutes

Watermelon pieces
Squeeze of lime juice
5½ (1g) scoops Shape It gel
   powder

In a food processor, blend watermelon pieces until you are left with the juice. Strain into a small saucepan through a fine sieve until you have 350ml of liquid. Add a squeeze of lime juice and gel powder.

Cook over low heat for 2 mins, then pour into a non-stick container, refrigerate until set. Portion as desired.

Tips: **Serve as part of our fruit salad. ~ Serve at room temperature.**

VANILLA & ALMOND SEMOLINA FUDGE

Serves 4
Prep 5 minutes
Cook 10 minutes

⅓ cup full cream milk
2 tbsp castor sugar
2 pinches ground cinnamon
2 tbsp almond meal
1 tsp butter
1 tsp vanilla essence
60g fine semolina
Extra virgin olive oil spray

Grease a square muffin pan, or any non-stick tray or container with olive oil spray. In a small saucepan, combine milk, vanilla, sugar, almond meal, butter and cinnamon and bring to the boil.

Reduce heat and slowly add the semolina. Stir continuously with a wooden spoon for 3 min, making sure there are no lumps.

Using a silicon spatula, portion into the mini square muffin, if needed spread with spatula to flatten it out. Give the top a quick spray with the oil, then cover with cling wrap. Allow to cool for 1.5 hours.

Once cooled, turn out and serve.

Tips: **Can use takeaway containers. ~ Serve at room temperature.**

COCONUT & MANGO
ICY POLE

*Serves 3 serves of
2 ice poles*
Prep 5 minutes
Cook 2 minutes

120g mango pieces
120ml coconut cream
160ml Greek yoghurt
1 tbsp milk powder
1 tbsp honey
8 (1g) scoops Shape It gel
  powder

In a food processor blend mango and coconut cream, scraping down the sides of the bowl with a spatula and re-blending 2-3 times until you have achieved a smooth consistency.

Transfer to a small saucepan, add gel powder, honey and milk powder, stir, simmering for 2 mins. Remove from heat, stir in yoghurt.

Pour mixture into icy pole moulds, tap to remove bubbles, insert icy pole sticks and place in the freezer for 1-2 hours or until it sets.

Tips: **You can use fresh or tinned fruit for this recipe. ~ Substitute mango with banana for variety ~ Another option is to freeze in a rectangular tray. Once frozen, cut into cubes and roll in shredded coconut. ~ Having seconds is a great idea for these icy poles to get more protein ~ Ensure no fluids from condensation remain on the plate—drain before serving.**

R S M P T Th1 Th2 Th3

YOGHURT CUBES

Serves 4
Prep 5 minutes
Cook 2 minutes

180ml milk
2 tbsp castor sugar
½ tsp vanilla essence
2 tbsp milk powder
240ml yoghurt
8 (1g) scoops Shape It gel
   powder
Extra virgin olive oil

In a saucepan, combine milk, sugar, vanilla and milk powder bring to a simmer. Add 5 scoops of gel powder, simmer for 2 mins.

Remove from heat and add yoghurt slowly, stir well until combined.

Spray a non-stick container with oil and pour in yoghurt mixture. Cover with cling wrap, and refrigerate until set.

Turn out onto a chopping board and cut into 3cm cubes, serve with modified fruit salad.

Tips: **Add to bircher muesli for an excellent breakfast. ~ Serve at room temperature. ~ Ensure no fluids from condensation remain on the plate/drain before serving.**

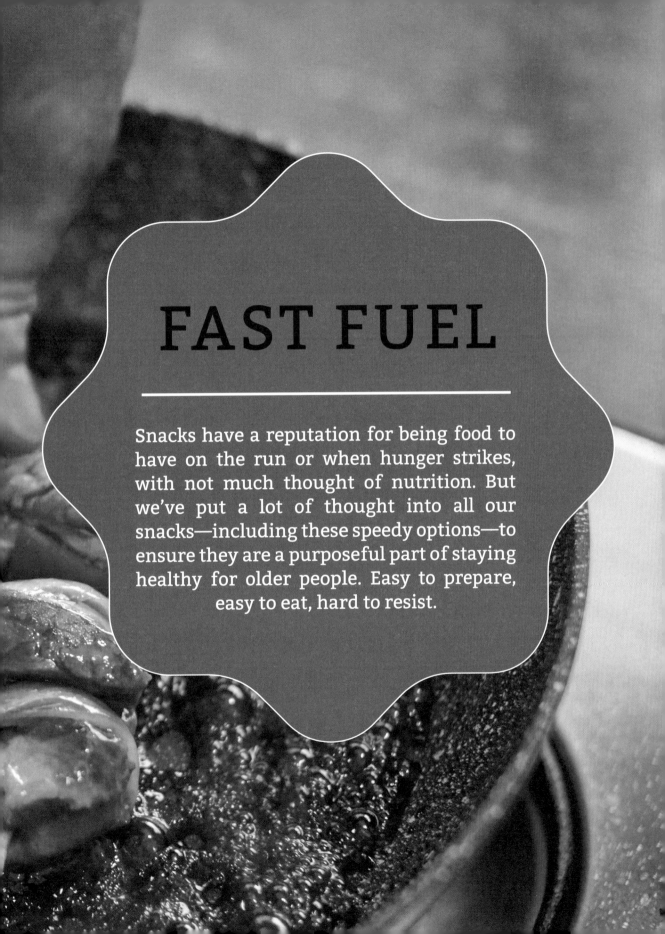

FAST FUEL

Snacks have a reputation for being food to have on the run or when hunger strikes, with not much thought of nutrition. But we've put a lot of thought into all our snacks—including these speedy options—to ensure they are a purposeful part of staying healthy for older people. Easy to prepare, easy to eat, hard to resist.

ASPARAGUS, PROSCIUTTO & CHEESE

Serves 4
Prep 5 minutes
Cook 8 minutes

12 spears asparagus (thin)
8 slices prosciutto ham
Basil leaves
100g bocconcini or buffalo
  mozzarella
Sea salt and pepper

Trim the ends of the asparagus spears, cook in boiling salted water for 2 mins and remove, refresh under cold water, pat dry.

Place 3 spears together into four piles, place 2 slices of prosciutto ham on flat surface and place about 25g of sliced mozzarella onto each of the four prosciutto wraps. Place a small basil leaf on the cheese and season with salt and pepper.

Place the spear bundles onto the four ham wraps and wrap the ham around the asparagus bundles neatly.

Refrigerate until needed, remove and bake in hot oven (200°C) for 8 mins on baking paper. Allow to cool slightly and serve.

Tips: **Substitute ham for bacon or other combinations of soft cheeses. ~ Does not freeze well.**

BACON WRAPPED PRAWNS

Serves 8 pieces/4 serves
Prep 5 minutes
Cook 2-3 minutes

200g uncooked prawns,
   shelled and deveined
   (about 8 large prawns)
4 rashers of bacon, rind
   removed

Marinade
2 tbsp extra virgin olive oil
2 tsp lemon juice
2 tsp chopped parsley
1 clove garlic chopped
Zest of ¼ lemon
Sea salt flakes and pepper
Skewers soaked in water

Mix all the marinade together until blended, place the prawns in the marinade, cover and refrigerate for a couple of hours.

Lay out the four strips of bacon on baking paper and place a piece on the top. Flatten the bacon with a rolling pin to make it thinner. Drain the prawns, cut the bacon in half making 8 pieces.

Wrap prawns with bacon and skewer with a toothpick or cocktail stick (remove after cooking). Preheat grill and brush the prawns with olive oil and grill, turnover after 2 mins and cook until prawns are cooked. Serve with skewer removed.

DATES WITH BACON & CREAM CHEESE

Serves 9 pieces/3 per serve
Prep 5 minutes
Cook 5 minutes

9 x (1x6 mm) pieces cream
cheese
9 pitted dates (preferably
Medjool)
9 roasted whole almonds
(optional)
6 slices bacon, cut crosswise
into thirds
9 wooden tooth picks

Preheat the oven to 200°C. Stuff one piece of cheese and one almond into each date, then wrap one piece of bacon around each date and secure bacon with a toothpick if desired.

Arrange dates with the bacon seam down and 4cm apart in a shallow baking tray. Bake 5 mins, then turn dates over with tongs and bake until bacon is crisp, 5 to 6 mins more.

Drain on a paper towel or parchment and serve immediately.

Tips: **This can also be made with buffalo mozzarella and prosciutto ham.**

FIGS WITH PROSCIUTTO

Serves 2 (3 fig halves each)
Prep 5 minutes

3 figs cut in half
6 slices prosciutto
Drizzle of extra virgin olive oil

Cut the figs in half and wrap each fig half in 2 slices of prosciutto, repeat until all figs have been wrapped drizzle with a little extra virgin olive oil.

Tips: **This is a simple but delicious recipe. ~ Goats cheese can also be smeared on the fig halves with cracked pepper to make this dish even more exotic.**

GRILLED BEEF KEBABS

Serves 2
Prep 5 minutes
Cook 6-8 minutes

½ Spanish onion,
   cut into wedges
200g scotch fillet, cut into
2cm pieces
½ red capsicum, deseeded
   and cut into 2cm piece
30ml extra virgin olive oil
1 crushed garlic clove
1 tbsp red wine vinegar
1 tbsp chopped parsley
Sea salt flakes and freshly
   ground black pepper
2 metal skewers or large
   bamboo skewers soaked
   in water for 30 mins.

To serve
1 small tub hummus
2 small pita bread pockets
2 tbsp Greek yoghurt

Thread the beef, onion and capsicum alternating on both skewers. Place on a plate and then mix 30ml of olive oil, crushed garlic, red wine vinegar and parsley. Cover the kebabs with the marinade and refrigerate for 2 hours.

Cook the kebabs on a barbecue plate for 6-8 mins, open 2 small pita breads and make a pocket, smear a generous dollop of hummus into each bread pocket remove the meat and vegetable from the skewers and place in each of the pita bread. Add a favourite relish and/or 1 tbsp of yoghurt in each pita pocket.

Tips: **Can also be served on its own on a plate. ~ If you don't have pita bread, an alternative is hot dog rolls. ~ Cheese is also great source of dairy protein to add to this great dish. ~ Tabouli is also tasty in the pita breads. ~ For a meat-free option, follow the recipe but omit the meat and add mushrooms.**

STUFFED DATES, GOATS CHEESE & WALNUTS

Serves 6 pieces/2 serves
Prep 5 minutes

60g goat's cheese
2 tbsp walnuts chopped
6 dates, pitted
½ tsp grated lemon zest
1 tsp lemon juice
1 tbsp chopped parsley
1 tbsp extra virgin olive oil
Sea salt flakes and freshly
   cracked black pepper

Place the cheese, walnuts and lemon zest in a ceramic bowl and mix with a spoon until combined. Add the lemon juice and chopped parsley. Season with sea salt and freshly ground black pepper.

Carefully open the dates, leaving one side attached. With a spoon, divide mixture into the 6 pitted dates, place on a plate and drizzle with a little extra virgin olive oil.

Tips: **Any type of soft cheese can be in used in place of the goat's cheese. ~ Also delicious wrapped in a slice of prosciutto.**

PICKLED SARDINES

Serves 3
Prep 5 minutes
Cook 10 minutes

150ml cider vinegar
150ml white wine vinegar
100g brown sugar
2 tsp sea salt
3 bay leaves
1 sprig thyme
10 black peppercorns
2 juniper berries
20 fresh sardine fillets,
   deboned and head removed
1 small Lebanese cucumber,
   sliced into thin rounds
1 small red onion, peeled and
   finely sliced
1 lemon, zested and cut into
   wedges

Place all the ingredients apart from the sardines, cucumber, onion and lemon zest in a pot. Bring to the boil and stir until all the sugar has dissolved. Remove from the heat and leave to cool.

When the brine has cooled to room temperature, pour into a shallow non-metallic dish. Add the sardine fillets (check for bones), cucumber, onion and lemon zest. Make sure everything is submerged in the liquid. Cover the dish in cling wrap (not foil) and leave in the fridge overnight. Will keep refrigerated up to 4 days.

Serve on toast or crackers with wedges of lemon.

Tips: **Ask your fishmonger to fillet your sardines for you, as it is a fiddly process.**

TERIYAKI CHICKEN SKEWERS

Serves 2
Prep 5 minutes
Cook 12-15 minutes

300g chicken thigh fillet
5 tbsp Japanese soy sauce
3 tbsp honey
Juice of 1 lime
1 clove garlic crushed
1 tsp chopped ginger
2 tsp sesame oil
4 wooden bamboo skewers
   soaked in water for 30 mins

Place the soy, honey and lime juice and ginger and garlic and sesame oil in a bowl and mix thoroughly. Place the chicken (diced into 25mm cubes—ask your friendly butcher) in the marinade and mix thoroughly and leave in refrigerator for 2 hours.

Remove from refrigerator and slide the chicken onto the soaked skewers. Brush remaining marinade over the skewers and spray with a little olive oil. Place on a hot barbecue and cook for 12-15 mins or until cooked through.

Remove from the skewers to serve.

Tips: **Serve with Greek salad or serve removed from skewer in a soft roll with good tomato sauce and salad. ~ Vegetables can be added to skewers and grilled.**

ITALIAN SAUSAGE WITH CHEESE AND BACON

Serves 8
Prep 5 minutes
Cook 10 minutes

4 x thin Italian sausages
100g mature cheddar cheese
4 rindless bacon rashers

Carefully cut the sausages lengthways half way through and slice cheese into thin, long matchsticks and lay inside the Italian sausage. Reform the sausages and chill for 30 mins. After 30 mins, wrap the sausages completely in the bacon strips.

Pre heat oven to 200°C and place the 4 sausages on baking paper on a non-stick baking sheet. Spray with a little extra virgin olive oil and bake for 10 mins or until the sausages are cooked through.

Cut each sausage in 3 and serve with grilled vegetables or roasted potatoes and asparagus.

Tips: **These can also be wrapped in puff pastry sheets and cooked like a sausage roll. ~ Great source of protein and energy.**

SANDWICH WRAP

If you think sandwiches are boring, think again. These recipes are anything but, and are also quick and easy to make. Sandwiches and wraps are a great option for smaller meals and are a dish everyone is used to eating with their hands.

CHICKEN SAUSAGE HOTDOGS

Serves 4
Prep 5 minutes
Cook 8 minutes

2 good quality thin chicken
    sausages
½ Spanish onion thinly sliced
½ red capsicum thinly sliced
1 tbsp butter
1 tbsp olive oil
1 leaf of iceberg lettuce
4 small hot dog rolls
Dijon mustard

Twist the sausages in half to make 2 smaller sausages, then cut the twists.

Heat butter in a frying pan over medium heat and add onion and cook until wilted and brown, then add capsicum and cook for 2 mins until it's soft. Remove from the heat and allow to cool.

Remove the capsicum and onion from the frying pan, add a little olive oil and cook the four small sausages. Slice the rolls lengthways. If 4 small rolls are not available cut 2 larger hot dog rolls in half.

The rolls can be lightly toasted under the grill. Remove and smear a little Dijon mustard on each roll, tear a piece of washed iceberg and place in roll, spoon relish on the iceberg lettuce and top with the warm sausages.

Tips: **Any type of sausages can be used and cheese is a great addition to the rollers.**

CHICKEN WALDORF SANDWICH

Serves 4 sandwiches
Prep 15 minutes

100g cooked chicken breast
  skin off, thinly sliced
½ small apple, cored and
  diced
½ celery stick ends, trimmed
  and thinly
40g walnuts, roughly chopped
60g (2 tbsp) whole egg real
  mayonnaise
½ tbsp chopped parsley or
  tarragon
8 slices soft white bread
Sea salt flakes and ground
  white pepper to taste
Soft butter

Heat a small saucepan of salted water and blanche the celery for 2 mins. Remove from water and cool under cold running water.

Place the chicken and celery, apple and walnuts on a large chopping board and chop finely ensuring all pieces are very small. Alternatively it can be pulsed in a food processor briefly.

Place the chopped chicken mix into a bowl, pour in the herbs and add the mayonnaise, fold through with a dessert spoon until all combined. Season to taste.

Butter the 8 slices of bread and divide the mixture onto 4 slices. Place the other slice on top and remove the crusts with a sharp serrated knife. Cut into triangles for an elegant high tea style treat.

Tips: **This mix will keep covered overnight, any longer and the apple will discolour.**

CROQUE MONSIEUR

Serves 2
Prep 5 minutes
Cook 15 minutes

4 thick slices of white bread
1 tbsp unsalted butter
2 thin slices gruyère cheese
2 thin slices prosciutto or
　leg ham
Freshly ground white pepper

Preheat the oven to 200°C. Butter each slice of bread and turn half the slices butter-side down on a tray. Cover these with a layer of cheese and ham or prosciutto, then repeat the layers. Season with pepper.

Top with the remaining slices of bread (butter-side up). Place the tray in the oven and bake the sandwiches for about 15 mins, or until the cheese is melted and the bread is golden.

Remove and cut each in half to serve.

Tips: **We recommend good quality bread such as sourdough or soft cob loaf. ~ Other great combinations include turkey, Swiss cheese and cranberry sauce or with sliced mustard fruits. ~ It is also great with a splodge of mustard pickle on the cheese.**

HAM & 3 CHEESE PANINI

Serves 2
Prep 5 minutes
Cook 5 minutes

4 slices of soft bread
50g ricotta
4 small slices buffalo
   mozzarella
100g sliced leg ham
¼ cup grated parmesan
   cheese
Sprinkle oregano leaves
Sea salt and cracked pepper

Top 2 slices of bread with ricotta, ham, mozzarella cheese and parmesan. Sprinkle with sea salt and cracked pepper and oregano. Place remaining bread on top. Brush both outsides of the 2 sandwiches with a little olive oil or use olive oil spray.

Heat a large frying pan with a little oil and place the 2 sandwiches down in the frying pan. Press the sandwiches down with a spatula or place a side plate on top to press them down.

When golden brown, carefully turn over and repeat until both sides are golden. Remove and cut into triangles and serve.

Tips: **Any combinations of cheese or meat are good for these protein rich sandwiches.**

PAULA WOLFERT'S AVOCADO SARDINE TOASTS

Serves 4
Prep 5 minutes
Cook 5 minutes

4 tbsp extra-virgin olive oil
2 tbsp chopped flat-leaf
    parsley
1 tbsp sherry wine vinegar
Salt and freshly ground
    pepper
2 (4½ ounce) cans
Portuguese whole sardines
    packed in olive oil
1 large firm, ripe Hass
    avocado
4 to 6 day-old, thin slices of
    country-style bread
4 scallions (white part only)
    cut lengthwise into thin
    strips about 1 inch long
Garnish
Chives

Make a parsley vinaigrette by whisking together the olive oil with the parsley and vinegar in a medium bowl. Season with salt and pepper to taste.

Drain the sardines, divide into fillets, and soak in the vinaigrette for at least 1 hour. For easier slicing, chill the avocado in the refrigerator for 1 hour.

Using a mandolin or a 1mm slicing blade, carefully slice the avocado paper-thin. Remove the skin and pit as you slice.

Grill the bread, turning once on a grill over hot coals or in a fry pan with a little butter or oil until nicely browned on both sides. Drain the sardine fillets and lightly brush the toasts with the vinaigrette.

Pile 3 or 4 slices of avocado onto each toast, top with a portion of the sardines, and scatter scallions (spring onions, shallots) and a few chives on top. Serve at once.

Avocados have been available to cooks in the Mediterranean since the sixteenth century, when Cortés brought them back from the New World. It was in Catalonia where I first tasted this simple dish, a combination of silky, paper-thin slices of ripe avocado and marinated fat strips of salty sardine fillets topped with crisp strings of scallions and chives, which makes for a great textural contrast — easy to duplicate and hard to forget.

The combination is based on a dish from the Canary Islands, but the brilliant execution is the work of the legendary master chef Ferran Adrià, famous for his culinary innovations, which include the use of foams, gelatinized liquid and savoury lollipops. —Paula Wolfert

Recipe © 2003 Paula Wolfert

SMOKED SALMON & AVOCADO RICE PAPER ROLLS

Serves makes 8 rolls
Prep 10 minutes

4 x 16cm rice paper rounds
125g smoked salmon
   (4 slices)
½ carrot, peeled and grated
1 small Lebanese cucumber,
   shredded
½ avocado, sliced thinly
8 mint leaves

Place the rice paper in a bowl of warm water for 10 seconds to soften. Place on a clean dry surface to soften further for 5- 10 seconds. Place the salmon in the centre, top with the cucumber and carrot and avocado and lay mint leaves down the centre.

Fold in 2 ends and wrap like a spring roll tightly. Cut each roll in half and serve immediately. They can be left covered with damp kitchen paper and wrapped in refrigerator for up to 60 mins, any longer and they start to dry out.

Tips: **These are versatile and any combination of filling can be added. ~ These rolls are soft and easy to eat. ~ All supermarkets stock the rice paper rounds.**

TUNA, CHIVES & CELERY SANDWICH

Serves 4
Prep 5 minutes

4 slices of white bread, lightly
   buttered
¼ stick celery, finely chopped
   80g canned tuna (in brine),
   drained
2 tbsp mayonnaise
1 tbsp chives, chopped
1 tbsp Spanish onion, finely
   chopped

Mix celery, chives and Spanish onion. Carefully add drained tuna and fold through and season with sea salt and ground white pepper. Spread the mixture evenly on 2 slices of bread. Top with the second slice of bread.

Trim off the crusts with a serrated knife and cut into 3 fingers, then cut these in half.

Tips: **Wet mixes are ideal for easy eating with less chance of the filling falling out. ~ This recipe can be adapted in many ways, try swapping the tuna with cooked chicken or crab.**

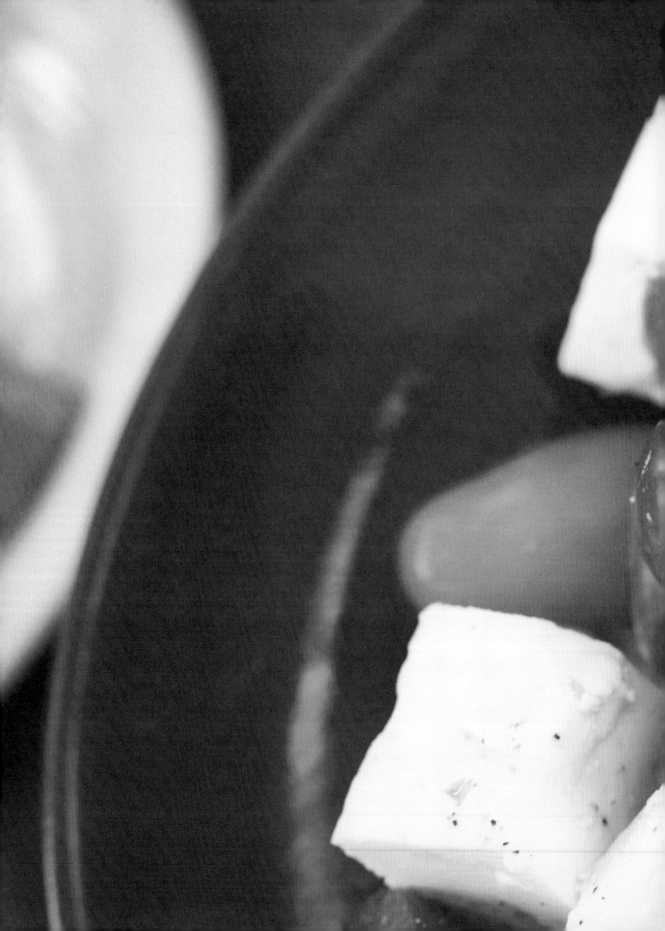

VEGIES, EGGS & DAIRY

There's a reason why vegies are the foundation level of the healthy eating food pyramid—they are vital to a balanced, nutritional diet. You'll love these hand-held vegetable snacks partnered usually with eggs and dairy to provide high nutrition and high protein.

BABY BOCCONCINI WRAPPED IN ZUCCHINI

Serves 12 pieces, 3 per serve
Prep 5 minutes
Cook 5 minutes

2 x 12cm length zucchini cut
lengthways in paper thin
    slices
100g baby bocconcini
Small bunch mint
Sea salt
Extra virgin olive oil

Spray the zucchini slices with extra virgin olive oil on one side and grill until golden on one side. Allow to cool, drain the liquid from the bocconcini and pat dry with absorbent kitchen paper towel. Wrap each piece of bocconcini in the zucchini strip and place a small mint leaf in each wrap.

Refrigerate until ready to serve, heat cheese balls for 30 seconds under grill to warm.

Tips: **All types of grilled vegetables can be used to replace the zucchini. ~ Soft cheese can also be used to replace the bocconcini e.g. brie wedges or camembert.**

INSALATA CAPRESE

Serves 3
Prep 5 minutes

200g roma tomatoes
150g bocconcini, thickly
    sliced
1 tbsp extra virgin olive oil
2 tsp balsamic vinegar
Sea salt flakes and freshly
    ground black pepper
⅓ cup picked basil leaves

Lay slices of tomato, bocconcini and basil leave alternatively in rows.

Tips: **Use fresh mozzarella instead. ~ Also works well if you cube other type of cheese and serve tossed with bite size cherry tomatoes and basil leaves.**

LENTIL & CHEDDAR LOAF

Serves 8 slices/2 per serve
Prep 10 minutes
Cook 45 minutes

2 cups cooked lentils, drained
250g grated cheddar cheese
1 small onion, finely chopped
1 tbsp soy sauce
¼ tsp ground black pepper
1 tsp sea salt flakes
1 cup white breadcrumbs
½ cup ground almonds
¼ tsp thyme
1 egg, beaten
1 tbsp soft butter

Blend the lentils, cheese and onions together. Add remaining ingredients and mix thoroughly. Bake in a greased small loaf tin for 45 mins.

Allow to cool, remove and cut into pieces.

Tips: **This does not freeze well, but if covered, will keep in refrigerator for a few days. ~ For a modified diet, serve the loaf warm or at room temperature, ensuring all crusts are removed.**

GREEK SALAD

Serves 2
Prep 5 minutes

1 Lebanese cucumber, cubed
1 punnet of bite sized cherry
   tomatoes
½ Spanish onion, quartered,
70g feta cut into bite size
   pieces
⅓ cup of Kalamata olives,
   pitted
Pinch of sea salt and cracked
   black pepper
Dress with a little extra virgin
   olive oil
Squeeze of lemon

Blanch Spanish onion in boiling water for 1 minute and drain. Place all ingredients in a bowl, drizzle with a little extra virgin olive oil and a squeeze of lemon. Season and serve.

Tips: **This is a great finger food accompaniment with most lunch snacks. ~ A robust snack that holds up at room temperature for an hour or so. ~ Cherry tomatoes are best bite-sized and a mixed colour range is ideal.**

ROASTED MEDITERRANEAN VEGETABLES

Serves 4
Prep 5 minutes
Cook 15-20 minutes

Large field mushroom,
   quartered
4 small zucchinis
½ Spanish onion, quartered
1 parsnip
4 Dutch carrots
100g sweet potato
4 cooked small potatoes
Sea salt flake
2 sprigs thyme
1 sprig rosemary
3 cloves garlic smashed with
   skin on
¼ cup extra virgin olive oil
1 tbsp chopped parsley

Peeled and quarter the carrots and parsnip, making sure to remove the woody stem. Peel and cut sweet potato into 4 large pieces. Cut zucchini in half lengthways. Place all root vegetables and cooked potato (skin on, cut in half) into a large roasting tray, drizzle with ¼ of the oil. Add the onion, herbs and garlic and toss into the oil. Season with sea salt and pepper.

Place oiled vegetables on baking paper in the roasting tray in a preheated oven (200°C). Remove after 10 mins, toss the vegetables and return to oven. Meanwhile, add 3 tbsp of the extra virgin olive oil in a frying pan and add the mushroom quarters and sauté.

Remove from frying pan. Keep warm and add another 3 tbsp of oil into the frying pan. Add the zucchini halves cut side down and cook until browned. Turnover and brown the s kin side.

Remove the cooked vegetables, add the warm mushroom and the cooked zucchini. Season to taste, sprinkle on chopped parsley and serve.

Tips: **A great vegetarian option which can be varied with other vegetables. ~ Grilled asparagus is great also in this medley. ~ Serve room temperature. ~ Great accompaniment for many recipes in the 'Super snacks' section.**

SPINACH, FETA & ZUCCHINI FRITTATA

Serves 2
Prep 10 minutes
Cook 25 minutes

1 tbsp extra virgin olive oil
½ Spanish onion, sliced thinly
Zucchini, sliced
Garlic clove, crushed
100g feta diced
1 cup baby spinach leaves
3 eggs
1 tbsp cream
80g grated cheddar
1 tsp sea salt flakes
2 tbsp chopped mint
½ tsp ground white pepper

Heat oil in a 30cm frying pan. Fry onions and zucchini until lightly golden. Add the garlic and cook for 1 minute. Add the spinach and cook until wilted and then remove from the pan. Drain off excess liquid from the spinach and zucchini.

Beat the eggs and cream together and add the seasoning and chopped mint. Heat a little olive oil in frying pan and return the onion, spinach and zucchini, spread evenly over the base of the frying pan and add the fetta.

Carefully pour the egg mixture over and place the frying pan on top of the stove, cook the bottom of the frittata for about 4 mins. Meanwhile turn on the grill then sprinkle the cheese over the frittata. Place the frying pan under the grill to cook the top (non-plastic handle).

Remove the cooked frittata and serve either warm or cold in wedges.

Tip: **Serve with egg wedges, cucumber sticks, cherry tomatoes and pitted olive salad.**

SWEET POTATO, LENTIL & SAGE TART

Serves 4
Prep 10 minutes
Cook 35 minutes

250g shortcrust pastry
  (see basic recipes)
½ can (200g) lentils, drained
750g sweet potatoes
½ cup sour cream
3 eggs
2 tbsp chopped sage
1 tbsp honey
2 tsp ground cumin
1 tsp grated nutmeg
1 tsp sea salt flakes
½ tsp ground white pepper

Either use half of shortcrust pastry in 'Basic recipes' or purchase pre-made shortcrust. Roll out the pastry until 3mm thick. Place the pastry in a 23cm greased tart tin and refrigerate.

Cook sweet potatoes in a saucepan of boiling salted water until soft. Drain, cool and place in a food processor with the sour cream and process until smooth.

Fold through the lentils, eggs, sage, nutmeg, honey, cumin sea salt and pepper. Spoon mixture over the pastry case.

Bake in a pre-heated oven (200°C) for 35 mins or until the filling is set and a golden colour. Allow to cool slightly, then cut into wedges

Tips: **Diced ham, prosciutto or cooked sausage mince can be added to this recipe. ~ Serve with steamed vegetables or asparagus spears.**

VEGETABLE BARS

Serves makes 12 bars/serves
Prep 15 minutes
Cook 25-30 minutes

¾ cup brown sugar
3 tbsp unsalted butter
1 large egg
1 tsp vanilla
1 cup whole wheat flour
1 tsp baking soda
¼ tsp sea salt
½ tsp cinnamon
Small zucchini, grated
Carrot, peeled and grated
 2 tbsp tomato paste
1 cup sultanas
¼ cup ground almonds
Pinch all spice
Frosting
4 cups cream cheese, softened
½ tbsp lemon juice
1¼ cup icing sugar

Beat the butter, brown sugar, egg and vanilla until smooth. Add the flour, baking soda, cinnamon, salt and all spice to the egg mixture. Mix gently. Add the grated vegetables, tomato paste, sultanas and ground almonds. Line a 20cm square cake tin and pour in the batter, tapping to knock out any air pockets.

Bake at 180°C for 25-30 mins or until springy to touch and golden brown. Cool on a wire rack.

Beat the cream cheese until light and fluffy and add the lemon and icing sugar until it is spreadable. Cover the top of the vegetable slab, which is cut in half and then into 6 slices each.

Tips: **Can be frozen. ~ Before freezing, wrap each piece individually in cling wrap.**

BASIC RECIPES

Our basic recipes are usually components of other recipes throughout the book but would also be great in your own creations! Some are suitable for modified diets.

HIGH PROTEIN MILK

Serves 8
Prep 2 minutes

1 cup skim milk powder
1L full cream milk

Using a 2L milk container, add 100g of milk powder to 1L of milk. Shake to combine and refrigerate until needed.

Tips: **High protein milk can also be purchased from the supermarket. ~ Substitute in all recipes containing milk to increase the protein content. ~ Can be used in milkshakes, smoothies, mashed potato and milk-based sauces.**

PERFECT HARD-BOILED EGG

Serves 1
Cook 2 minutes

1-2 free range eggs

Place eggs in a saucepan of cold water. Use eggs at room temperature—if they're too cold, the shells may crack.

Place saucepan over medium heat and bring to a simmer while stirring in one direction. The movement helps to centre yolks.

For soft-boiled eggs, cook for 4 mins; for semi-firm yolks, cook for 5 mins; and for hard-boiled, cook for 8 mins.

PIZZA BASES

Serves makes 2 bases
Prep 2.5 hours

3 tsp dried yeast
½ tsp sugar
1 cup of warm water
2 cups plain flour
3 tbsp olive oil
½ tsp sea salt

Place the yeast and sugar in a bowl and add a little of the water. Leave to ferment for 5 mins. Add flour, rest of the water, olive oil and salt and knead together until silky smooth dough is formed. Knead for about 5 mins.

Place the dough in a clean bowl and cover with a damp cloth and leave in a draft free warm area for about 1-2 hours.

Knock back the dough and knead again, roll out to a thickness of ½ cm on floured cling bake paper. This can be frozen for later use or any left -over dough stored in refrigerator.

SWEET SHORTCRUST PASTRY

Serves 500g
Prep 15 minutes

1 cup unsalted butter,
    chopped
2 eggs
1 cup icing sugar
2 cups plain flour

Cream butter and eggs. Sift together flour and sugar.

Place dry ingredients in a bowl, add butter and eggs and work in dry ingredients until a dough forms. Add a little water to adjust the dough if need be.

Refrigerate for 30 mins before rolling out. It freezes well, but if left in a refrigerator for a couple of days, it will oxidise.

PULLED BEEF/PORK

Serves 6-8
Prep 10 minutes
Cook 4 hours

1kg beef blade roast or pork
   shoulder, bone in
½ Spanish onion, sliced
2 garlic cloves, finely chopped
1 red chilli, finely diced
1 tsp ground cumin
1 tsp ground coriander
1 tsp dried parsley flakes
2 cups (500ml) beef stock
1 cup (250ml) tomato passata
50ml red wine vinegar
2 tsp olive oil
Salt and pepper

Preheat oven to 160°C. Season the beef or pork with salt and pepper, heat oil in a large frypan over a medium to high heat, add the beef and sear well all over until the beef is nicely browned, around 5-6 mins. Transfer to a small roasting tray, not much larger than the beef.

Reduce the heat and sauté onion, garlic and chilli in the frypan until translucent. Add spices and stir until fragrant. Add the beef stock, passata and vinegar and bring to a simmer. Adjust seasoning if needed. Pour onto the beef and cover tightly with foil.

Place in the oven and cook for 3½ to 4 hours. Remove the beef once it is tender and pulls away from itself with a fork. Add all the liquid to a saucepan and reduce by around half, until you are left with a thick sauce. Using a fork, pull the beef while it is still hot. Check the seasoning of the sauce and adjust if necessary, and then add the shredded beef back into the sauce.

Tips: **Use this recipe to make empanadas, featured on page 72. ~ Pulled beef is great to have on hand for quick meals—reheat and pop in a wrap with some lettuce, cucumber, tomato and hummus. ~ Can also be used as a sandwich filling, in a pie or a quiche, or even added to an omelette with some cheese and sautéed mushrooms.**

(R) (S) (T) (Th1) (Th2) (Th3)

SHORTCRUST PASTRY

Serves 2
Prep 10 minutes

2 cups plain flour
1 cup cornflour
1 cup chopped butter
2 eggs

Sift dry ingredients, make a well in centre and place softened butter and eggs in the centre and mix together with your fingers. If you find the pastry is too dry add a little water.

Refrigerate for 30 mins.

SOUR CREAM PASTRY

Serves 2
Prep 45 minutes

2½ cups plain flour
Pinch of sea salt
180g butter
1 egg

Sift the flour and salt into a bowl, add softened butter and rub in with your fingertips until like fine bread crumbs.

Mix the egg and sour cream together, then add to the flour and make dough. Wrap in cling wrap and refrigerate for 30 mins.

Remove pastry and roll between 2 pieces of baking paper, then use in your recipe as instructed.

MEAL PLANS

Our meal plan ideas support smaller portions, mid meals, eating more regularly and finger food approaches. They cover regular diet, vegetarian diet and modified diets—soft, minced and pureed. Although these meal plans are designed with six meals in a day, they could also be spread across eight smaller meals.

These meal plans and many recipes included in this book are high in energy and protein which is ideal for many older people and people with dementia.

For all the meal plans, it is important to remember that fluids must be thickened if this is a person's dietary recommendation, including drinks and smoothies.

Finger food diet (regular texture)
*Fluids must be thickened for those who require it.

Breakfast	Continental breakfast Tea or coffee * Water *
Morning tea	Iced coffee *
Lunch	Fish and chips Cherry tomatoes, cucumber slices Juice or water *
Afternoon tea	Prune and almond cake Tea or coffee *
Dinner	Grilled chicken, fig salad with sweet potato Flourless chocolate cake Juice or water *
Supper	Milk to drink*

Vegetarian finger food diet (regular texture)
*Fluids must be thickened for those who require it

Breakfast	Perfect hard-boiled egg Toast fingers with butter Tea or coffee * Water *
Morning tea	Stuffed dates, with goat cheese and walnuts Tea or coffee *
Lunch	Spinach fetta and zucchini frittata Potato pieces and carrot sticks Juice or water *
Afternoon tea	Welsh fruit bread Tea or coffee *
Dinner	Sweet potato, lentil and sage tart cake Lime yoghurt cake Juice or water *
Supper	Milk to drink*

Soft finger food plan
* Fluids must be thickened for those who require it.

Breakfast	Hot smoked salmon and mascarpone pate Soft bread (without crust) Tea or coffee * Water *
Morning tea	Strawberry smoothie *
Lunch	Baked ricotta Carrot puree pieces Spinach and sweet potato Juice or water *
Afternoon tea	Brownie Cheese cake Tea or coffee *
Dinner	Lentil and cheddar loaf Spinach and sweet potato Yoghurt cubes Sliced banana Juice or water *
Supper	Milk to drink*

Finger food meal plan for minced diet

* Fluids must be thickened for those who require it.

Breakfast	Apple and strawberry Bircher muesli squares Yoghurt cubes Perfect pear puree Tea or coffee * Water *
Morning tea	Mango lassi *
Lunch	Puree chicken drumsticks or fillet slices Ham, mozzarella and butter bean slice Creamy broccoli Juice or water *
Afternoon tea	Vanilla, semolina and almond fudge Tea or coffee *
Dinner	Pulled pork terrine Smooth vanilla carrots Cauliflower and cheese puree slice Yoghurt cubes Apricot puree slices Juice or water *
Supper	Milk to drink*

Meal plan suitable for pureed diet

* Fluids must be thickened for those who require it.

Breakfast	Apple and strawberry Bircher muesli squares Yoghurt cubes Pete's puree peaches Tea or coffee * Water *
Morning tea	Chocolate, banana and almond smoothie*
Lunch	Puree chicken drumsticks Pumpkin and semolina fudge Juice or water *
Afternoon tea	3 cheese panna cotta Tea or coffee *
Dinner	Salmon puree fillets Pea puree Puree parsnip and sweet potato Yoghurt cubes Hand-held puree watermelon Juice or water *
Supper	Milk to drink *

Meal plan nutritional goals

The nutritional goals for each recipe have been based on the work done for the Queensland Meals on Wheels Nutrition Manual. Goals for meals across the day and meal plans were based on a minimum 76kg reference male at 126kJ/kg/day = 9.6mJ, 1.2g protein/kg/day = 91.2g. Most recipes included in this book are high in energy and protein as dietary restrictions are not warranted unless specifically recommended by a health professional for individuals.

Main meals (lunch and dinner) when provided at recommended serving size provide at least 1800kJ of energy and 25g of protein. Lighter meals including breakfasts provide at least 1200kJ and 10g protein per serve. Mid meals at recommended serving size provide at least 600kJ and 5g of protein. Most desserts provide at least 1500kJ and 5g protein. If a small serve is preferred it would be about two thirds of a normal serve.

If anyone prefers less salty foods or requires a low salt diet for a medical reason, we suggest you omit any added salt mentioned in the recipes and purchase reduced salt products.

CONTACTS AND RESOURCES

Information in this section covers helpful contacts and resources in Australia but similar stockists, support organisations and food suppliers will be available in most countries. The Dementia Centre operates internationally.

Commercial thickener information

When thickening fluids for people with dysphagia, it is important that recipes are tried and tested to ensure they are not placing a person at risk of aspiration.

The most commonly used thickeners are listed below. Although the recipes in this book have been formulated with particular products, we do not necessarily endorse that product and each person should decide for themselves which product they prefer. However, when following recipes, you will need to pay particular attention to the amounts of powder and modify quantities according to the product you have purchased.

Further retailers for thickening agents, who sell products to individuals (rather than companies, such as hospitals and nursing homes) may be found on the Internet. It is recommended that you complete your own research where possible to find competitive pricing. Remember, those who are part of the Department of Veterans' Affairs may be eligible for subsidised products.

Flavour Creations: Instant thick powder, pre-thickened fluids and innovative dysphagia and nutrition products

Stockists of Flavour Creations for each Australian state and territory can be found by visiting www.flavourcreations.com.au and clicking on the 'where to buy' page or by phoning head office on 07 3373 3000.

Flavour Creations developed Shape It powder, a gelling stabiliser, to support many of our modified meals and this product and others are expected to be available from crackingrecipes.com

Nestle: Resource ThickenUp Clear powder

Stockists for ThickenUp Clear for each Australian state and territory can be found by visiting www.nestlehealthscience.com.au and typing "ThickenUp in the search bar or by phoning or 1800 671 628.

Gelea and Spuma Instant

Gelea Instant and Spuma Instant are available from Biozoon Food Innovations, part of Prestige Products Group Pty Ltd. Visit www.molecular-gastronomy.com.au, phone 1300 652 198 or email sales@prestigeproducts.com.au

Food moulds

Puree Food Molds

Online ordering system at
www.pureefoodmolds.com or
email info@pureemolds.com

Prestige products

www.molecular-gastronomy.com.au or
phone 1300 652 198.

Also, keep watching crackingrecipes.com
for the supply of moulds and other products
to assist in the creation of our modified meal
recipes.

Online food suppliers

If it is difficult to get to the shops and markets
for your own ingredients, these options may
assist.

Aussie Farmers Direct

www.aussiefarmers.com.au or phone
1300 645 562 (8am–8pm Monday to Friday,
8:30am–5pm Saturday AEDST).

Coles online

www.shop.coles.com.au or phone 1800
455 400 (Monday to Friday, 6am–midnight,
Saturday 7am–10pm and Sunday 8am–6pm
AEDT).

Woolworths online

www2.woolworthsonline.com.au or phone
1800 000 610 (Monday to Friday, 6am–10pm,
Saturday 6am–10pm, Sunday 8am–6pm)

Dementia-related support organisations

Dementia Centre

The Dementia Centre, part of HammondCare,
works to empower everyone from people
with dementia and carers to health
professionals and managers to partner in
improving quality of life for people living
with dementia. Our service offers evidence-
based practice advice drawn from extensive
and ongoing research programs, backed by
experience in the field. The Dementia Centre
provides services to people living across
Australia and internationally including the
United Kingdom.

Australia: phone +61 2 8437 7355 or visit
www.dementiacentre.com.au Address:
Dementia Centre, Pallister House,
Greenwich Hospital, 97-115 River Road
Greenwich, NSW 2065 Australia.

Dementia Behaviour Management Advisory Services (DBMAS)

The DBMAS program is an Australian
Government initiative which provides clinical
support for people caring for someone with
dementia who is demonstrating behavioural
and psychological symptoms of dementia
(BPSD) which are impacting on their care.
It provides a 24-hour a day helpline as well
as face to face visits. DBMAS is also the
point of referral for residential aged care
providers seeking assistance from the
Severe Behaviours Response Team (SBRT).

Phone 1800 699 799 or
visit www.dbmas.org.au

Alzheimer's Australia

Alzheimer's Australia provides information and education on dementia and runs programs and services such as counselling and support groups.

Phone 1800 100 500 or visit www.fightdementia.org.au

My Aged Care

My Aged Care is a service run by the Australian Government Department of Health that provides useful information and advice on all areas of aged care, including community care, nursing homes, staying at home and staying healthy.

Phone 1800 200 422 (8am–8pm Monday to Friday, 10am–2pm Saturday) or visit www.myagedcare.gov.au

Independent Living Centre

The Independent Living Centre is a service, staffed by occupational therapists, that provides independent and impartial information and advice about equipment (such as adaptive cutlery, special cups), assistive technologies and home modifications.

The national website is www.ilcaustralia.org and provides links to state branches.

Eating, drinking support organisations

Speech Pathology Australia

Speech Pathology Australia can provide information about speech pathology services and help locate local speech pathologists. Phone 1300 368 835 or visit www.speechpathologyaustralia.org.au

Dietitians Association of Australia

Dietitians Association of Australia provides general information about food and diet and can help locate local dietitians. Phone1800 812 942 or visit www.daa.asn.au

Occupational Therapy Australia

Occupational Therapy Australia supports the work of occupational therapists and can assist in finding an occupational therapist in your area. Phone 1300 682 878 or visit www.otaus.com.au

REFERENCES

Chapter 2

Alzheimer's Disease International statistics
www.alz.co.uk/research/statistics
Accessed 30 March, 2016

Chapter 4

Dietitians Association of Australia. DAA Evidence based practice guidelines for the nutritional management of malnutrition in adult patients across the continuum of care. Nutrition & Dietetics Journal 2009; 66: S1-S34.

http://onlinelibrary.wiley.com/doi/10.1111/ ndi.2009.66.issue-s3/issuetoc Accessed 13 November 2012

Rist G, Miles G, Karimi L. The presence of malnutrition in community-living older adults receiving home nursing services. Nutrition & Dietetics 2012; 69: 46–50

Chapter 5

Cichero J, Steele C, Duivestei J, Clav P, Chen J, Kayashit J, Danta R, Leck C, Speye R, Lam P, and Murray J. The Need for International Terminology and Definitions for Texture-Modified Foods and Thickened Liquids Used in Dysphagia Management: Foundations of a Global Initiative. Swallowing Disorders (RE Martin, Section Editor). Current Physical Medicine and Rehabilitation Reports December 2013, Volume 1, Issue 4, pp 280-291.

Morgan-Jones P, Colombage E, McIntosh D, and Ellis P. Don't give me eggs that bounce. 2014. HammondCare Media: Sydney, Australia.

Meal plans

References: Meals on Wheels Nutrition Manual, Nutrition guidelines for the provision of home delivered meals. Angela Malberg 2012. Queensland Meals on Wheels Association Inc. Strathpine Centre, QLD 4500 Australia.

NUTRITIONAL INFORMATION

Recipe Name	Energy (kJ)	Energy (cal)	Protein (g)
Apple and strawberry bircher muesli squares	894	213	5.6
Apple bran smoothie	699	167	5.1
Apricot puree pieces	215	51.4	0.83
Asparagus, prosciutto and cream cheese	738	177	16.4
Baby bocconcini wrapped in zucchini	615	147	7.2
Bacon and egg cups	1211	290	24.6
Bacon and egg pie	2299	550	24.6
Bacon muffins with cream cheese and spinach	1268	303	13.1
Bacon wrapped prawns	352	84	9.0
Baked ricotta	579	138	11.4
Bean quesadillas	857	205	7.6
Bec's banana and coconut bread	1393	333	5.3
Breakfast cookies	640	153	3.3
Bubble and squeak cakes with bacon	3831	917	31.7
Carrot puree pieces	505	120	1.7
Cauliflower cheese puree slice	696	166	5.6
Ceylon tea punch	667	160	0.7
Cheese, ham and chive croquettes	538	129	6.2
Chicken empanadas	4004	958	30
Chicken sausage hotdogs	1063	254	12.5
Chicken fillet slices	641	153	17.9
Chicken waldorf sandwich	2010	481	15.4
Chicken, sweet potato and bean cakes	1117	267	14.7
Chocolate cheesecake brownie	1271	304	5.0

Fat (g)	Carbohydrate (g)	Fibre (g)	Calcium (mg)	Iron (mg)	Page
4.9	34.5	4.9	100.4	1.15	126
4.4	24.4	3.7	120.5	1.6	116
0.17	10.3	2.1	11.0	0.28	146
11.7	0.8	1.1	180.0	0.8	156
11.7	2.2	1.4	251.7	0.6	186
12.9	17.2	2.3	63.1	2.6	39
42.1	18.5	0.8	203.7	1.7	42
18.1	20.9	1.9	123.8	1.1	40
5.2	0.2	0.2	35.7	0.4	158
9.2	1.4	0.1	230	0.5	128
11.4	15.9	3.0	141	1.07	52
21.7	28.2	3.2	36.7	1.2	58
6.1	20.6	2.0	34.4	0.8	36
78.8	18.9	4.4	515.6	1.5	85
9.8	6.0	2.7	56.7	0.18	130
14	4.2	2.0	144.6	0.36	132
0.2	36.4	2.8	71.5	0.6	118
8.6	6.3	0.4	126.1	0.2	54
60.9	70.1	5.1	69.6	2.6	72
13.4	19.8	2.6	58.6	1.2	172
7.6	3.7	0.3	57	0.63	143
32.2	31.4	3.0	54.3	1.4	174
7.2	33.5	3.6	54.9	1.7	74
19.5	27.9	0.8	27.7	0.6	102

Recipe Name	Energy (kJ)	Energy (cal)	Protein (g)
Chocolate truffles	1648	394	5.7
Chocolate, banana and almond smoothie	753.5	180	7.1
Cinnamon stickies	1310	313	4.6
Coconut and mango icy pole	444	111	2.3
Continental breakfast	1693	405	24.7
Cornish pastie	5062	1211	41.0
Creamy broccoli	463	110	2.7
Croque monsieur	1649	394	19.1
Date , apple and sultana slice	1583	379	2.7
Dates with bacon and cream cheese	1036	248	11.6
Duke of Devonshire's Nut Biscuits	2074	493	7.7
Farmworkers breakfast skillet	1938	464	24.2
Figs with prosciutto	955	228	17.1
Fish and chips	3000	718	43.3
Flourless chocolate cakes	1689	404	6.3
Ginger ale	190	45	0
Greek salad	1007	241	7.6
Grilled beef kebabs	2025	484	29.6
Grilled chicken and fig salad with sweet potato	1837	439	30.6
Grilled lamb cutlets, asparagus, kipfler potatoes and mushrooms	1712	410	16.9
Grilled lamb meatballs	2270	543	24.3
Ham and cheese English muffin French toast	737	176	12.6
Ham and three cheese panini	738	176	12.6
Ham, mozzarella and butter bean slice	1541	369	13.7
High protein milk	598	143	10.2
Hand-held puree watermelon	280	66.9	1.05
Hot smoked salmon and mascarpone pate	1232	295	15.3

Fat (g)	Carbohydrate (g)	Fibre (g)	Calcium (mg)	Iron (mg)	Page
36.0	10.1	2.9	95.1	1.8	104
8.4	17.5	3.2	169.7	0.9	120
13.4	43.3	2.9	58.8	1.1	60
5.3	12.5	0.7	63.6	0.23	151
27.5	12.3	2.9	340.9	1.5	38
66.0	106.9	8.6	73.0	5.2	76
9.8	3.0	1.4	47.9	0.28	129
15.9	41	3.1	242	1.5	175
14.8	58.1	4.3	62.0	1.5	61
35.1	35.1	5.2	37.2	1.6	160
35.3	37.7	2	85.9	1	106
35.3	9.9	4.3	36.4	2.6	46
14.6	6.2	2.5	33.7	0.7	160
26.9	70.6	8.1	128.8	3.3	78
23.9	41.8	3.2	51.8	2.8	108
0.3	11.4	0.25	3.3	0.045	117
21.0	4.2	2.4	186.5	0.9	188
29.6	22.8	4.4	78.2	3.1	162
20.7	30.9	5.3	64.3	1.3	80
33.1	9.3	3.2	16	2.4	82
38.0	23.7	5.4	201.5	2.8	84
6.4	15.2	1.4	173.8	0.6	44
6.4	15.2	1.4	173.8	0.6	176
18.8	35.1	2.2	128.8	0.4	141
4.5	15.8	0	336.7	0.08	198
15.2	14.6	1.5	13	0.8	149
25.8	0.4	0.3	41.5	0.4	56

Recipe Name	Energy (kJ)	Energy (cal)	Protein (g)
Iced coffee	1711	409	15.2
Insalata caprese	1262	302	14.8
Italian sausage with cheese and bacon	949	227	13
Japanese BBQ pork	1141	272	17.1
Korean style hamburger	1024	245	22.2
Lamb kofta	678	162	16.6
Lentil and cheddar loaf	2686	643	34.7
Lime yoghurt cake	1898	454	9.5
Maggie Beer's ginger coconut slice	773	185	3.1
Pan fried salmon, sweet potato, asparagus and tomato	1490	356	26.9
Parsnip and sweet potato	585	146	2.3
Paula Wolfert's avocado and sardine toasts	2141	512	18.4
Pea puree	642	153	5.5
Pete's puree peaches	233	55.7	0.7
Peanut and sultana cookies	436	104	2.1
Perfect pear puree	158	37.7	0.1
Perfect hardboiled egg	272	65	6.4
Pickled sardines	1022	244	17.0
Pizza bases	3124	747.3	16.7
Pizza Margherita	2824	675	21.2
Portuguese tarts	556	133	2.5
Prune and almond cake	2173	520	10.7
Pulled beef	1013	242	27.3
Pulled pork terrine	625	149	18.2
Pumpkin and semolina fudge	975	233	5.7
Puree chicken drumsticks	1975	472	26.2
Roasted baby potatoes with Italian sausage	2337	559	24.7
Roasted Mediterranean vegetables	801	192	3.2

Fat (g)	Carbohydrate (g)	Fibre (g)	Calcium (mg)	Iron (mg)	Page
18.6	47.1	0	470	0.29	117
24.7	3.7	1.8	548.6	0.6	186
18.7	1.6	0.6	90.5	0.6	169
15.4	15.1	2.4	18	1.2	86
9.6	16.6	1.5	22.8	1.6	88
9	2.7	1	107.9	2.9	90
33.5	45.5	8.0	569.6	3.8	187
19.4	59.9	2.5	114.5	0.9	110
14.7	9.7	1.9	26.0	0.7	105
19.5	16	4.6	44.3	2.3	92
9.8	10.1	2.3	58.9	0.25	138
40.6	17.5	2.9	272.0	2.2	178
10.06	8.9	4.4	60.4	1.36	140
0.09	12.1	1.4	5.3	0.3	146
5.9	10.7	0.7	6.7	0.3	62
0.03	6.7	2.2	4.4	0.08	148
4.3	0.2	0.0	24.0	1.0	198
2.5	35.1	1.8	680.9	4.1	166
29.5	99.9	6.3	31.1	2.2	199
11.5	54.6	5.4	375	1.6	94
5.8	17.7	1.0	27.4	0.5	64
32.2	44.0	4.3	93.6	1.5	66
12.8	3.5	1.5	25.6	2.9	200
3.3	7.3	0.5	18.6	0.7	144
14.4	19.5	1.9	110.9	0.56	139
40	2.5	0.02	73.2	0.45	142
37.5	28.4	4.5	261.6	2.2	57
15	8.7	4.0	39.1	1.0	190

Recipe Name	Energy (kJ)	Energy (cal)	Protein (g)
Roasted peaches and cream popsicles	305	73	2.7
Salmon puree fillets	1603	383	16.9
Salmon burgers	3499	837	49.5
Sardine fritters	2007	480	24.5
Sausage & spinach (breakfast) tortilla	2913	697	24.0
Scotch eggs	3521	842	32.3
Shortcrust pastry	1519	363	5.2
Smoked salmon rice paper rolls	487	117	8.1
Smooth vanilla carrots	509	121	1.8
Sour cream pastry	1465	350	5.6
Southern fried chicken	3741	895	49.0
Spiced mango lassi	809	193	7.6
Spinach and sweet potato	597	142	2.8
Spinach, feta and zucchini frittata	2401	574	31.7
Strawberry smoothie	472	113	5.5
Stuffed dates, goats cheese and walnuts	1242	297	6.2
Sweet potato puree	608	145	2.4
Sweet potato, lentil and sage tart	2713	649	17.3
Sweet shortcrust pastry	1752	419	5.3
Teriyaki chicken skewers	1586	379	30.6
Three cheese panna cotta	1244	297	9.4
Tuna, celery and chive sandwich	572	137	5.2
Vanilla and almond semolina fudge	1095	262	5.2
Vegetable bars	2224	532	10.3
Watermelon and almond smoothie	1268	303	8.2
Welsh fruit bread	1580	378	6.4
Wholemeal raspberry bars	1691	405	5.3
Yoghurt cubes	851	203	6.0

Fat (g)	Carbohydrate (g)	Fibre (g)	Calcium (mg)	Iron (mg)	Page
2.1	10.6	0.7	89.7	0.19	112
34.7	1.7	0.06	47.0	0.8	135
30.5	85.6	7.3	629.9	4.8	87
34.9	16.5	1.6	403.0	2.4	96
64.0	5.1	4.6	104.9	3.9	48
54.7	53.8	4.7	107.7	4.2	98
22.2	92	1.3	18.8	1.5	201
5.6	7.4	1.4	31.0	0.3	180
9.8	6.1	2.8	57.08	0.2	131
22.3	31.25	1.6	23.1	0.7	201
65.1	28.4	2.4	76.2	3.6	97
3.2	32.3	2.5	217	0.6	122
9.9	10.0	2.8	85.4	0.68	134
45.7	6.8	4.9	579.4	3.5	192
3.2	14.7	1.5	175	0.39	123
15.7	31.3	4.9	41.2	1.3	164
9.8	11.6	2.1	54.8	0.3	133
32	67.6	10.9	210	5.4	194
25.7	42.1	1.2	17.1	0.7	199
12.1	37.1	1.15	32.1	1.9	168
26.6	6.0	0.34	284.4	0.12	127
8.4	9.9	0.7	15.0	0.5	182
16.2	24	1.1	108.3	0.4	150
34.7	45.5	2.9	98.5	1.1	195
18.5	25.1	3.3	182.1	1.6	116
8.4	68.0	3.8	74.8	1.4	68
21.9	45.2	5.3	34.5	1.6	55
10.1	23.1	0.3	196.9	0.07	152

CONVERSIONS

Our conversion charts are particularly detailed in consideration of the safety aspects of preparing texture-modified diets.

1 teaspoon = 5ml
1 tablespoon (Australian) = 4 teaspoons
1 tablespoon (UK) = 3 teaspoons (½ fl oz)
1 cup = 250 ml (8 fl oz)

1.25L	5 cups	44fl oz
1.5L	6 cups	52fl oz
2L	8 cups	70fl oz
2.5L	10 cups	88fl oz

Weight conversions

10g		¼oz	
15g		½oz	
30g		1oz	
60g		2oz	
90g		3oz	
125g		4oz	(¼lb)
155g		5oz	
185g		6oz	
220g		7oz	
250g		8oz	(½lb)
280g		9oz	
315g		10oz	
345g		11oz	
375g		12oz	(¾lb)
410g		13oz	
440g		14oz	
470g		15oz	
500g (½kg)	16oz	(1lb)	
750g		24oz	(1½lb)
1kg		32oz	(2lb)
1.5kg		48oz	(3lb)
2kg		64oz	(4lb)

Liquid conversions

metric	cup	Imperial
60ml	¼ cup	2fl oz
100ml		3½fl oz
125ml	½ cup	4fl oz
150ml		5fl oz
185ml	¾ cup	6fl oz
200ml		7fl oz
250ml	1 cup	8¾fl oz
310ml	1¼ cups	10½fl oz
375ml	1½ cups	13fl oz
430ml	1¾ cups	15fl oz
475ml		16fl oz
500ml	2 cups	16fl oz
625ml	2½ cups	21½fl oz
750ml	3 cups	24fl oz
1L	4 cups	32fl oz

Cup measures

1 cup almonds whole	110g	3½oz
1 cup flaked almonds	125g	4oz
1 cup banana mashed	240g	7½oz
1 cup basil leaves 50g		1¾oz
1 cup berries frozen	125g	4oz
1 cup breadcrumbs soft	60g	2¼oz
1 cup breadcrumbs dried	125g	4½oz
1 cup grated cheese 125g	4½oz	
1 cup couscous	190g	6¾oz
1 cup chocolate, chopped	150g	5oz
1 cup desiccated coconut 90g	3¼oz	
1 cup thickened cream	250g	8oz
1 cup plain flour	135g	4½ oz
1 cup golden syrup	380g	13oz
1 cup honey	400g	14oz
1 cup icing sugar	125g	4oz
1 cup lentils	185g	
1 cup rice	155g	5½oz
1 cup rolled oats uncooked100g	3½oz	
1 cup yoghurt 250g	8oz	
1 cup caster sugar	225g	
1 cup brown sugar	200g	

Oven temperatures

Celsius (electric)	Celsius (fan forced)	Fahrenheit	Gas mark
120°	100°	250°	1 very slow
150°	130°	300°	2 slow
180°	160°	350°	4 mod
190°	170°	375°	5 mod hot
200°	180°	400°	6 hot
230°	210°	450°	7 very hot
250°	230°	500°	9 very hot

ABOUT THE AUTHORS

Peter Morgan-Jones

Peter Morgan Jones is Food Ambassador and Executive Chef at HammondCare, where it is his role to inspire and maintain a rich and vibrant food culture. He has a long global career as a successful chef. He was assisted in Chapter One by Emily Colombage, an Accredited Practicing Dietitian who loves food and works with older people and people living with dementia at HammondCare. Both were co-authors of *Don't give me eggs that bounce*.

Lisa Greedy

Lisa is an Accredited Practicing Dietitian working as a HammondCare residential aged care dietitian. She has also worked in consultation with the Dementia Centre. Her major interests include dementia, nutrition, food service, menu design and small group education. She has worked in aged and dementia care for many years where she incorporates into every day practice her passion for food, cooking, gardening and nutrition. She is committed to advocating for better food quality for older people and improving nutritional outcomes for people living with dementia.

Prudence Ellis

Prudence is a Senior Speech Pathologist at HammondCare's Greenwich and Neringah Hospitals. She works with adults in aged care, palliative care, rehabilitation, and oncology rehabilitation. Prudence also has experience in residential aged care, and within the community. She has a focus on development of resources and training packages for resident care. Her role also includes clinical education, with supervision of students from many universities in Sydney. She is passionate about improving the quality of life of people with dementia and with swallowing difficulties, and was a co-author of *Don't give me eggs that bounce*.

Danielle McIntosh

Danielle is a Senior Dementia Consultant with the Dementia Centre, HammondCare. She is an Occupational Therapist and has considerable experience working with adults with cognitive and neurological disorders. For more than a decade, Danielle has been involved in caring for people with dementia at home and in residential care, dementia-suitable design, and behavioural needs support and care planning. Danielle is a sought after conference presenter and co-author of three previous dementia-related books, including *Don't give me eggs that bounce*.

Lisa Greedy, Danielle McIntosh, Peter Morgan-Jones and Prudence Ellis chatting with resident at HammondCare Miranda.

Acknowledgments

The authors would like to thank the following people for their contributions to recipe development, meal testing, nutritional analysis, writing, editing and review, as well as the many people who have personally supported and inspired the authors in their work:

People living with dementia, older people, carers, family members, care workers, health professionals, cooks and chefs across Australia and beyond who have joined the discussion about beautiful food for people with dementia, older people and people with swallowing difficulties. And especially the residents, clients, families and staff from HammondCare services for all their feedback and suggestions.

Maggie Beer and her foundation for ongoing support and for continuing to be a powerful voice for better food for older people.

HammondCare chefs Belinda Chapman—for extensive work with recipes—and Peter Welfare for ongoing support. Leanne Galea and Emily Colombage (contributing author) for nutritional analysis.

Sybil Beattie, Kerry Gilsenan, Vanessa Arratia, Julie Cichero and Peter Lam for swallowing information and advice. Peter Hallett, Christina Maurice, Leigh Hatcher, Richard Knight and Tiffany Johnson for publishing support. The Fodera family for use of their beautiful home and kitchen.

Also, special thanks to our family and friends.

Thanks also to HammondCare for an inspiring food culture and A/Prof Colm Cunningham and the Dementia Centre for advice and support.

To everyone who purchased and publicised our first cookbook, *Don't give me eggs that bounce: 118 cracking recipes for people with Alzheimer's*, thanks for making this second book possible. Now they can be purchased as a bundle—crackingrecipes.com

And to all those for whom eating is not as easy as it was and for those who support them—thanks for your inspiration—bon appetit!

Index

First published by HammondCare Media 2016
Sydney Australia
hammondcaremedia@hammond.com.au
hammondcare.com.au   dementiacentre.com.au

ISBN 9780987582898

Cover and internal design: Melissa Summers of SD creative
Photography: Matt Jewell
Artistic consultant: Janette Fodera
Printing: 1010

National Library of Australia Cataloguing-in-Publications Data
Creator: Morgan-Jones, Peter, author.
Title: It's all about the food not the fork! : 107 hard to resist meals in a mouthful / Peter Morgan-Jones,
Lisa Greedy, Prudence Ellis, Danielle McIntosh.
ISBN: 9780987582898 (paperback)
Notes: Includes bibliographical references and index.
Subjects: Cooking. Cooking for the sick. Older people—Nutrition. Dementia—Diet therapy—Recipes.

Other Creators/Contributors: Greedy, Lisa, author. Ellis, Prudence, author. McIntosh, Danielle, author.
Dewey Number: 641.563

While the authors have exercised due care in ensuring the accuracy, reliability and safety of the material
contained in this book, it is provided for informational purposes only and is not intended as a substitute
for advice from your local doctor, medical specialist, speech pathologist or dietitian. The information in
this book is not intended to be used to diagnose, treat, cure or prevent any disease, nor should it be used
for therapeutic purposes or as a substitute for your own health professional's advice. The authors do not
accept liability for any injury, loss or damage incurred by use of or reliance on the information contained
in this book.

The recipes contained in this book have been carefully tested to produce the desired food consistency
and texture. However the authors cannot guarantee results due to a number of variable factors
including cooking conditions, inputs varying across brands and products being subject to change over
time. Accordingly, all care must be taken on each occasion when applying the recipes to verify that the
consistency and texture of the food is appropriate and safe for its intended us.

*Please note: some photos of food and meals may not fully reflect our recommendations regarding
contrast but are included for creative purposes.*

For the latest news on It's all about the food not the fork! and to purchase related products, share tips,
recipes and feedback, visit crackingrecipes.com